East Asia in Old Maps

EAST ASIA
IN OLD MAPS

HIROSHI NAKAMURA

THE CENTRE FOR EAST ASIAN CULTURAL STUDIES

TOKYO

EAST WEST CENTER PRESS

HONOLULU

c/o The Toyo Bunko
147, Kamifujimae-cho, Bunkyo-ku, Tokyo

This book was originally published with
the assistance of UNESCO, in implementation of
the Major Project on
Mutual Appreciation of Eastern and Western Cultural Values.

Distributed outside Japan by
EAST WEST CENTER PRESS
HONOLULU, HAWAII 96822

Printed in Japan by
KASAI PUBLISHING & PRINTING CO.
(*Pan-Pacific Press*)
Minato-ku, Tokyo.

2nd printing, July, 1964

Preface

This is an abridged version in English of Dr. Hiroshi Nakamura's treatise: "Tōa no Kochizu" (History of Mapping of the Eastern Asia) published in the Journal of Yokohama Municipal University, Series A-19, No. 88, March 1958. As very little is known in Japan or elsewhere about the maps of ancient East Asia the book will doubtless prove to be of great interest to the general public.

It is our great joy to state that Dr. Nakamura gave us ready consent when we approached him with our proposal to make his above-mentioned work suitable for publication in the series of books which the Centre for East Asian Cultural Studies intends to issue as reading for the non-specialist circle. In accordance with our aim, which consists in showing the change of image of East Asia in Orient and Occident in the course of time, special stress had to be laid on some parts of the original work at the sacrifice of other sections, for want of space. Consequently it was inevitable, to our great regret, that the author had to make a good deal of curtailing and to leave out entirely his learned notes containing much important information for the students of cartography. I earnestly solicit those who are versed in Japanese to consult Dr. Nakamura's original treatise for details.

During the whole process of reduction and translation Dr. Nakamura has never grudged time in order to meet our requirements, for which our most sincere thanks are due to him. I should like to mention here that Dr. Naka-mura has prepared in English a book on maps of ancient Japan made by Europeans—the fruits of scholarly effort which, when published, will certainly contribute very much to our knowledge of early cartography.

There remains now my pleasant duty of acknowledg-ing kindness and cooperation received from all quarters. As the publication of this book has been made possible by a subvention of Unesco, I wish first of all to express my thanks for this generous support. My debt of gratitude is also due to the authorities of the National Commission for Unesco in Japan for their usual good offices.

On sending the books to the world I would accompany it with my wish that it could answer the purpose of promoting mutual appreciation of Eastern and Western cultural values.

March, 1962.

TSUJI Naoshirō
Director of the Centre for
East Asian Cultural Studies

CONTENTS

Page

Preface

    I. Maps of East Asia in the Marco Polo Age 1

    II. Maps of East Asia in the Columbus Age 13

    III. Maps of East Asia in the Age of World Discoveries 19

    IV. Influences that the Portuguese Capture of Malacca and Expedition to Moluccas Gave on the Map 28

    V. Magellan's Circumnavigation and Spanish-Portugal Scramble over Spice Islands 35

    VI. East Asia on the Maps of the Dieppe School of North France 47

    VII. Influence of Portugal's Trade with China and Japan on the Maps of East Asia 49

    VIII. Spain's Jealous Attachment to Spice Island ... 56

    IX. Spanish Rule over the Philippines 61

    X. Iberian Cartographers' Contributions to the Mapping of East Indies 65

    XI. Maps Used by the Japanese Licensed Trading Ships 74

Imago Mundi (15th century). British Museum.

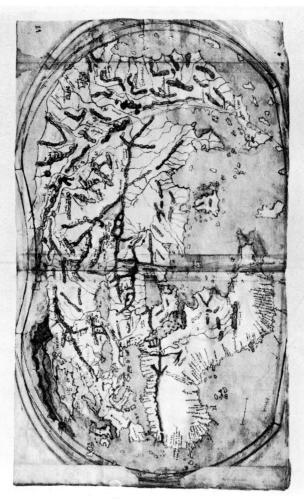

World map (1489).   Biblioteca Laurenziana, Florence.

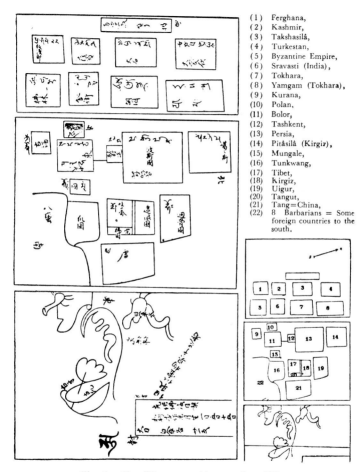

(1) Ferghana,
(2) Kashmir,
(3) Takshasilâ,
(4) Turkestan,
(5) Byzantine Empire,
(6) Sravasti (India),
(7) Tokhara,
(8) Yamgam (Tokhara),
(9) Kurana,
(10) Polan,
(11) Bolor,
(12) Tashkent,
(13) Persia,
(14) Pitâsilâ (Kirgiz),
(15) Mungale,
(16) Tunkwang,
(17) Tibet,
(18) Kirgiz,
(19) Uigur,
(20) Tangut,
(21) Tang=China,
(22) 8 Barbarians = Some foreign countries to the south.

Fig. 1. Sino-Tibetan world map of c. 733
(Onjoji Temple, Author's Photo).

Fig. 5.   Anonymous world map, attributed to Columbus
(Bibliothèque Nationale, Paris).

Hoc orbis Hemifphærium cedit regi Lufitaniæ.   Hoc orbis Hemifphærium cedit regi Hifpaniæ.

CVM PRIVILEGIO INVICTISSI=
mi Romanorum imperatoris Caroli quinti,ad quin=
quennia,ne quis uel typis excudat uel excudendos cu
ret hos codices geographicos,uns cū globis,fub mul
cta amittendorum exemplariū aliaq; pæna princi=
pis feuerieate inferenda.

Fig. 7.   Franciscus Monachus, De Orbis Situ, Antuepiæ, 1527
(British Museum).

Fig. 2.   Fra Mauro, bronze
            bust.   (Biblioteca
            Marciana, Venice).

Fig. 3.   Behaim's terrestrial
           globe 1492 (From
           E. L. Stevenson).

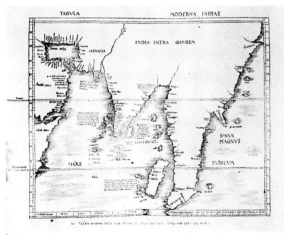

Fig. 6.   Ptolemy's Geography, Strasbourg 1513
           (Facsimile-Atlas, p. 19).

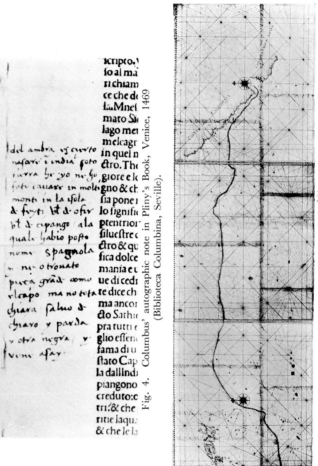

Fig. 4. Columbus' autographic note in Pliny's Book, Venice, 1469 (Biblioteca Columbina, Seville).

Fig. 13. Spanish Chart showing the Philippines-Mexico route, 1770 (Archivo General de Indias, Seville).

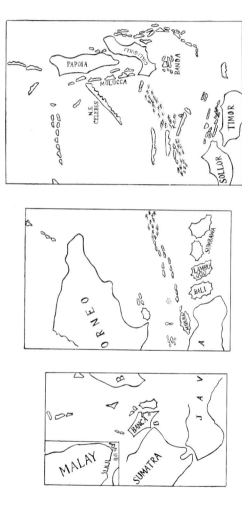

Fig. 8. Javanese map of East Indies, known as "Rodriguez' map" (Santarem's atlas, 1849).

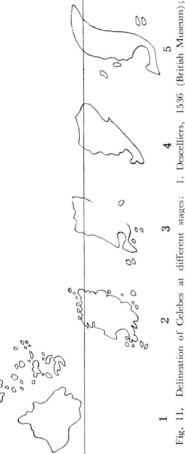

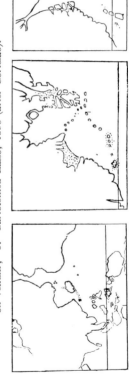

Fig. 11. Delineation of Celebes at different stages: 1. Descelliers, 1536 (British Museum); 2. Desliens, 1541 (after Hantzsch & Schmidt); 3. Lopo Homem, 1554 (Mus. d. Strum, Antich., Florence); 4. Ex-Marquis Ikeda's anonymous and undated chart on vellum; 5. Bartolomeu Lasso, 1590 (after Cortesão).

1   2   3   4   5

Fig. 12. Different types of Japan. 1. G. Mercator, 1569; 2. Diogo Homem, 1558 (British Museum); 3. Vaz Dourado, 1573 (British Museum).

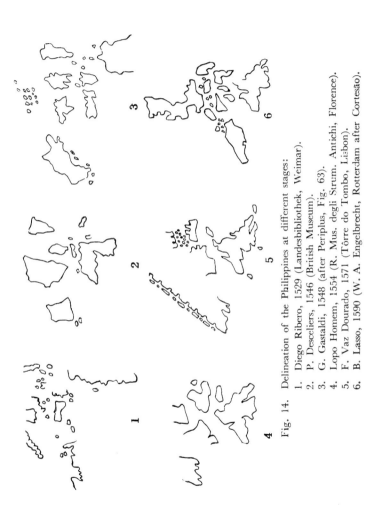

Fig. 14. Delineation of the Philippines at different stages:

1. Diego Ribero, 1529 (Landesbibliothek, Weimar).
2. P. Desceliers, 1546 (British Museum).
3. G. Gastaldi, 1548 (after Periplus, Fig. 63).
4. Lopo Homem, 1554 (R. Mus. degli Strum. Antichi, Florence).
5. F. Vaz Dourado, 1571 (Tôrre do Tombo, Lisbon).
6. B. Lasso, 1590 (W. A. Engelbrecht, Rotterdam after Cortesão).

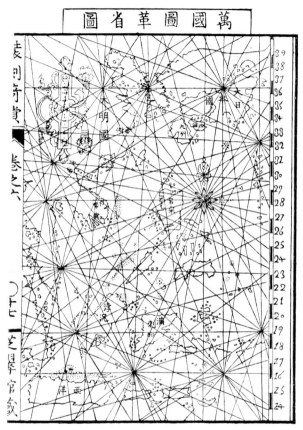

Fig. 15. Chart used by Japanese licensed merchantmen. Wood-cut print in 'So-ken-ki-sho'. ('Swords ornaments'). 1781.

East Asia in Old Maps

I. Maps of East Asia in the Marco Polo Age

It is believed to be more than 2,000 years ago that ancient peoples of both East and West drew their first maps. The Chinese, in the East, began their map-making in the Han dynasties (2nd century B.C. to 2nd century A.D.) and made remarkable progress in the T'ang (7th to 9th century), Sung (10th to 12th century) and Yüan (13th to 14th century) dynasties. However, their maps of East Asia were actually maps of China itself, with little reference to other parts of East Asia. On the other hand, the maps drawn by Arabs, which have important bearings on the cartography of East Asia, had no direct influence over later ages.

The most orthodox path leading to the modern maps of East Asia originated from Greek maps, drawn by the astronomical method of locating, which was introduced by Ptolemy. His method of map-making was long neglected and forgotten during the Medieval Age, but was restored during the Renaissance. Since then, map techniques have been improved steadily in parallel with development of navigation techniques, accelerated by the invention of the magnet compass and nautical astronomy, and by the consequent inventions of Portolanos and the Age of the Great Discoveries, brought to the present form. In this regard, maps of East Asia owe their development greatly to map-making of Portuguese and Spaniards, who were actively engaged in exploration and commercial practices in East Asia from the 16th century on. This essay is an attempt to trace back the above-mentioned path of map development in East Asia through old maps.

East Asia was first known to the West by Chinese silk (*serikon* in Greek, *sericum* in Latin). However, the word Sêres did not necessarily mean the Chinese. In fact, Sêres stands for several peoples located alongside the so-called Silk Road, which connected China with the West through Central Asia. Besides the Silk Road route, Chinese silk was transported by traders and navigators to the West through India to Mesopotamia and Egypt. Those who took this southern route called it after China where the silk was produced, namely Sin (Thin), possibly because of the name Ch'in, the empire of Shih Huang Ti (reigned 246–210 B.C.).

The second century witnessed very active East-West trade and commercial exchanges. And it was Ptolemy's book known as *'Geography'* that gave a scientific system to the rich geographical knowledge brought to Alexandria (which prospered as the commercial, traffic and cultural center of the world at that time). This book is no doubt one of the greatest scientific asset of the old days inherited by the present. It is often said today that his map can be favorably compared with modern maps in its accuracy. However, the accuracy of Ptolemy's map is limited to the Mediterranean coast area alone. His attempt to draw the map of East Asia, about which he had little knowledge, with the clearly established astronomical method of fixing longitude and latitude, made his map all the more confusing to posterity. His astronomical method itself was unpeccable, but his knowledge of East Asia was extremely poor.

Ptolemy's concept of East Asia is, in a nutshell, made up of continents surrounding the Indian Ocean (*Mare Indicum*) —the part of the ocean south of the equator was called *Mare Prasodum*—as Hipparchus (2nd century, B.C.) had believed. The Indian Ocean was believed to be surrounded by India and the Great Peninsula east of the Ganges in the north; the Sin (China) coast in the east; an unknown, tropical continent in the south; and Arabia and Ethyopia in the west. Between Sin and the Great Peninsula east of the Ganges was a gulf called *"Magnus Sinus"*, while India east of the Ganges (*India Extragangem* or *Transgangem*) and Sin were adjacent to Scythia or Serice across the northern Imaos mountain ranges. North of Scythia or Serice was unknown. In the Indian Ocean were several islands. The most outstanding of them was called "Taprobana."

Although Ptolemy's Geography is one of the most important sources for the study of old maps, it was totally neglected during the long Medieval Dark Age. As research on the classics flourished during the Renaissance, the Greek original was translated into Latin, and the book came suddenly into the limelight. It was the beginning of the so-called "Ptolemy's revival period." Ptolemy's Geography is now available in a variety of old copies, some of them artistic masterpieces in fine colors. With the invention of printing, there appeared some incunabula and gothics of Ptolemy's Geography. Thus, the book is considered to have been published in about 60 different versions, including the Greek original, Latin translation and modern language versions. In addition, about 30 different versions of "Pseudo-editions of Ptolemy," i.e. geographical treatises based on Ptolemy's Geography, are believed to have been published from the 16th century on.

Meanwhile, these new versions of Ptolemy's Geography were supplemented by the new maps (*Tabula Nova* or *Tabula Moderna*) which were drawn on the basis of geographical discovery during the 15th and 16th centuries. These supplemented new maps present valuable sources for research on cartographical history. Moreover, there are numerous works by commentators, expounders and researchers on Ptolemy's Geography. Therefore, not a few expert bibliographers are engaged in the study of Ptolemy's Geography today.

While the Greeks were highly scientific in their approach to map-making, as one can see from Ptolemy's maps, the Roman were very practical. It is often said, "The Greeks measured the earth by the stars and the

Romans by milestones." Of many itineraries made during the Roman Age, the most well-known was the "Itineraria" of the world (the world known to the Romans at that time), drafted during the reign of Julius Caesar (100–44 B.C.) and completed during the Augustus (63 B.C.–14 A.D.) era. The Itineraria, consisting of decsriptive and iconographic parts, was unfortunately lost. However, a copy of the iconographic part of it was found by a certain Conrad Celtes in late 15th century, and was studied by Konrad Peutinger (1465–1547), famous German archaeologist. This copy is generally known as *"Tabula Peutingeriana."*

This Itinerary, made in Constantinople under the region of Constantine the Great (273–337) during 337–338, was a world map, and the extant copy is lacking the westernmost part (Britania). The Itinerary has been studied and reproduced by several students since. In the East Asian part of the map were such countries as Sera Major, Cotiara, Mons Imeus, Mons Clacas, Abyos Scythæ and Xatis Scythæ, and such islands as Insula Dorados, Insula Taprobana, Insula Arcirse and Insula Solar. However, the description of the East Asian part of the map was generally incomplete. Moreover, there are a few other Medieval Itineraria extant today on the routes from Western countires to the Holy Land (Palestine), which cover less area than *"Tabula Peutingeriana."*

Since Constantine the Great ended the disorders in the Roman Empire and approved Christianity, the religion spread all over the empire and was believed even by Germanic races who were constantly invading the empire at that time.

The Christian faith was deeply rooted in people's minds even during the Medieval Dark Age which followed the collapse of the West Roman Empire in 476. The flat circular map of the world born from the meditation of monks and philosophers was the origin of the "Imago Mundi" or "Mappæ-mondi." There are ten or so of these maps of the world, drawn before the 13th century, existing now. One of them, most simply diagrammed, is made of a circle, which is subdivided into a semi-circle and two quadrants. One of the two quadrants stands for Europe, the other quadrant for Africa, with the Mediterranean, between them. And the remaining semi-circle indicates Asia. Between the semi-circle for Asia and the two quadrants for Europe and Africa lie Tanais (Sea of Azov), Pontus Euxinus (Black Sea), and the water system connecting the eastern Mediterranean and the Nile. The circumference stands for the vast ocean surrounding the world. Such a schematic map of the world, however, does not necessarily indicate the standard of geographical knowledge at that time. Such maps were miniatures or illustrations inserted in books of the time, which were incidentally inherited by posterity. Some of these maps depict the geographical features of several Mediterranean coast countries with a fairly realistic touch. And yet, they were drawn in strong religious color, with Jerusalem located at the center of the world, Terrestrial Paradise on the eastern tip of Asia, and with Adam and Eve as well as saints and angels depicted around the map.

The Saracens who emerged in Western Asia in the 7th century prospered after Al Mansur founded the capital in Bagdad (762). The Saracen culture reached its peak under the reign of Al Rashid (786–809) and Al Mamoun (813–833). Al Mamoun, in particular, gave special consideration to protection and promotion of the astronomical, mathematical, geographical and medical sciences. He had scientists of the time translate Ptolemy's works into Arabic and measure the distance of meridian degree.

The Saracen Empire's territorial expansion and trade development worked, on the one hand, as a factor to increase the geographical knowledge of the Saracens and to give impetus to the development of cartography by the astronomical observation method, and, on the other, promoted the exchange of East-West culture. Of a variety of scientific techniques introduced from China to Europe by the Saracens, the paper manufacturing method brought about a revolutionary development of techniques for making books in Europe, where papyrus and parchment had been used as book materials until then. Meanwhile, the importing from China of the magnet and the compass had a unique influence on traffic and consequently on cartography in Europe. The compass was transmitted to Mediterranean mariners during the second crusade period (1147–1149), and formed the basis for the so-called Portolanos in later years, a kind of marine chart indicating direction, distance and ports.

The maps drawn by the Arabs are studied by many modern cartographers. Among others Konrad Miller made a detailed study on 275 Arabian maps in 1926. Most of the Arabian maps are schematic, comprising geometric patterns such as the rectangle, the circle or simple curves. But world maps drawn by Edrisi in 1154 and several others show fairly realistic conformation.

Now, it is worth mentioning that a Sino-Tibetan World map is preserved in Onjōji Temple at Mii, not far from Kyoto. It is among many valuable documents brought to Japan from China in 858 by a famous Japanese priest, Enchin (814–891) who is better known by his posthumous title, Chishō-Daishi. The map bears, besides the Chinese, another inscription in an unknown language, which was not deciphered until Prof. Teramoto identified it as the Tibetan recently. With this language remaining unidentified, the map was facsimiled from century to century and there are several facsimile copies extant today. The map embraces a vast area, the whole world then known, and presents geographical features of 22 countries by a variety of geometric patterns. This manner of schematic drafting betrays its Arabic origin. According to Teramoto's study the original map might have been drawn in 733 or thereabout and is the first example of early Arabian maps introduced to China under the T'ang dynasty through Central Asia. In this regard, the simple and grotesque map is one of the rare cartographical monuments.

Fig. 1.

The invasion of Mongolians to Europe in the early 13th century horrified the Christians in Europe. Pope Innocent IV summoned a conference in Lyons to discuss counter-measures, and sent Giovanni Plano Carpini, the Franciscan, to Mongolia as a peace mission in 1245. French King Louis IX (St. Louis) also sent Monk Guillaume de Rubruquis of the same sect to the Mongolian court in 1253. One of the motives for the dispatch of such a mission to the pagan country was the legendary belief among Christians that there was a powerful Christian king called "Presbyter John" in East Asia who was to conquer pagans during those evil days to save Christianity. This legend spread amnog the Christians in Europe since the middle of the 12th century. And they believed that the Mongolian king was this Presbyter John himself. The legend survived through the 15th and 16th centuries, but with some modification—some maps of that time showing him as an African King and others as an Indian King. Much new knowledge on East Asia was brought back to Europe by these missions. Since such knowledge was not published until the 16th century, however, it had little influence on European cartography before the 16th century.

On the other hand, the Travels of Marco Polo had a tremendous influence on the development of geography and geographical discovery in later years. Marco Polo (c. 1254–1324) accompanied his father, Nicolo Polo, a Venetian merchant, on a journey to Mongolia in 1271 when he was only 17 years old. The father and son arrived in China in 1275 and were given an audience with Kubilai Khan, the Emperor of Yüan dynasty. The bright son, who was given special favor by Kubilai, stayed in China for 17 years, and left Zaitun (Chang-chow) by sea in 1292 for Il-Khanids in Persia, then returned home in 1295. Later, he joined the Venice-Genoa battle and was captured. It was when he was in the prison that he narrated his famous travels to his fellow inmate, Rusticiano. His travels were too fantastic to the eyes of the contemporary people to be believed immediately. However, the book he wrote had an increasing influence on posterity. There are about 90 old manuscripts of the book now existing, and about 100 new and old versions of the book. In addition, partial extracts of the text, studies and commentaries were published in abundance. Marco Polo's descriptions of Zipangu (Japan), Java, Sondur, Condur, Peutan (Bintang), Java Minor (Sumatra), Necuverum (Nicobar), Angamanain (Andaman), Ceylon, Madagazcar, Zangibar, etc., were far more accurate than the conventional European geographical knowledge of the East transmitted from the Arabs. It is often said that his description of the wealth and prosperity of Japan and China in his book had stimulated Columbus to set sail on his World Exploration tour and consequently gave impetus to the emergence of the Age of World Discoveries in the 15th and 16th centuries.

There exist several maps drawn on the basis of geographical knowledge of East Asia held by European travelers of the Marco Polo age. The question of whether or not Marco Polo himself made this kind of map has been discussed by many students. While Gezelius said it was almost certain that Marco Polo himself did not make maps of his travel, Count Teleki observed that the mural maps of the Sala Dello Scudo at Doges' Palace in Venice must have been drawn under the supervision of Marco Polo shortly after his return to Venice from China. As Dahlgren pointed out in detail, however, the mural maps (world map) drawn in the 14th century were destroyed by fire in 1483 and redrawn in 1553 by Giacomo Gastaldi, the famous cartographer of that time; these were again partly damaged by a new fire in 1574 and at last almost renewed by Fransesco Griselini in 1762.

In fact, it is apparent at first sight that this map was not of the Marco Polo age, judging from the fact that the part of East Asia on this map was drawn together with the western part of North America. However, Pullè maintains that the map presented by the Republic of Venice to Dom Pedro of Portugal in 1462 must be either Marco Polo's work or its copy. In addition, as many other students hold, Ramusio mentioned in his Collection of Voyages (published in 1550) the tradition of the fine marine chart and world map which were allegedly brought back by Marco Polo from East Asia. Therefore, there is an indication that there existed the maps that Marco Polo brought back from East Asia. Henry Yule, the authority in the study of Marco Polo, tried to restitute Marco Polo's world map. But the reconstructed map is largely in the category of Imago Mundi.

It is evident that if Marco Polo had brought back the maps from China, the maps would have been close to the Chinese map of the Yüan dynasty. For, there was a very accurate *'Yü-ti-t'u'* (World map, 1311–1320) drawn by Chu Szǔ-Pen (1273–1335 or 1340) of the Yüan dynasty in China. Although this map was actually completed after Marco Polo left China, the above assumption is not entirely impossible, because the geographical features of China in the *'Yü-ti-t'u'* were similar to those in *'Fo-tsu-tung-chi'* (1269–1271) edited by Chih P'an, a Buddhist priest of the Southern Sung period.

Some of the maps drawn from the geographical knowl-edge of travelers to East Asia during the Marco Polo age are still extant today. 'L'Atlas Catalan de Charles V,' of 1375 now preserved in the Bibliothèque Nationale at Paris, is one of them. East Asia in the map was drawn mainly on the basis of Marco Polo's Travels, according to Cordier, the famous sinologue. In the world map, drawn on parchment (anonymous, of 15th century) now preserved in the Biblioteca Estense in Modena; in the oval world map, also drawn on parchment, anonymous, of 1447, known as the "Genoa World Map," preserved at the Biblioteca Nazionale in Florence; in the fine, *Fig. 2.* large-sized, hand-written world map by Fra Mauro, of 1459, preserved at the Biblioteca Marciana in Venice; and in the brass circle plate world map of the 15th cen-tury, called "Stefano Borgia World Map," after the name of the former owner of the map, preserved at the Collegio de Propaganda in Rome—the Asian part is believed to

have been made in compliance with the knowledge of
Marco Polo and other travelers to the East. However, all
of these maps were drawn with the conformation of the
Imago Mundi type as its basis, with the inscriptions
about the East furnished by the travelers to the East. In
this sense, they differ in conformation widely from the
Chinese maps of the world Marco Polo was believed to
have brought back from China.

II. Maps of East Asia in the Columbus Age

The oldest extant terrestrial globe, made on the basis
of Marco Polo's knowledge of East Asia, is now preserved
at the Germanic National Museum in Nuremberg. This
globe ("Erdapfel") was made by Martin Behaim (1459–   *Fig. 3.*
1507), a German who served King John II of Portugal
and joined a Portuguese expedition to Africa. He made
this terrestrial globe in his home town in 1492, the year
Columbus discovered the New World. In this regard, this
globe is one of the data convenient for considering the
geographical knowledge of cosmographers at that time
and that of Columbus, too. A number of students have
made a detailed study on this globe. In addition, there
are scrupulous facsimile copies of it, now kept at the
British Museum, Bibliothèque Nationale in Paris, and
the American Geographical Society in New York.

The conformation of East Asia in Behaim's terrestrial

globe is characterized by the four peninsulas projecting
from the Asian Continent into southern oceans. The
westernmost peninsula of the four extends to Daho (Diu
Island, near the southern tip of Kathiawar Peninsula),
while the second peninsula from the west reaches Cape
Comorin. The third one is the Malay Peninsula, which
was known by ancients as Aurea Chersonesus (Golden
Peninsula). The easternmost, largest is a huge projection
extending to 30°S. lat., and is shaped like a horse leg,
just as the Malay Peninsula. It has no special name, but
let us call it the "Gigantic Peninsula" for convenience.

Such a fantastic figure as this Gigantic Peninsula originated from the conception that the part beyond the
eastern extremity of Ptolemy's World map is made up of
an ocean. This can be demonstrated by the fact that the
East Asian coast line runs almost straight from north to
south in many maps of that time. This was a very clever
manipulation from the part of cartographers, not to hurt
Ptolemy's authority on the one hand and on the other to
cover the unknown surface of the earth up to 360°,
which they filled with ocean. According to Level's study,
it can be shown by the writings of Toscanelli that the
deformation was first invented in Italy, then introduced
into Portugal. Of maps bearing the Gigantic Peninsula,
early products were mostly drawn by the Italians. The
Gigantic Peninsula was the most conspicuous feature of
the maps drawn during the transient period between the
period of classic cartography and the age of World Explorations, and remained in maps throughout the 16th

century, as will be mentioned later. The fact that there exist today more than 70 kinds of these maps, bearing the Gigantic Peninsula, from the 15th and 16th centuries, proves the ubiquity of the concept of the Gigantic Peninsula at that time.

Why, then, was the existence of the Gigantic Peninsula, a prdouct of the imagination, believed by geographers for so long a period? These reasons are conceivable. In the first place, Ptolemy's authority was so firmly established that it was hard to revise his concept of the world. Secondly, the geographical knowledge of Marco Polo and other travelers concerning East Asia was not convincing enough to refuse Ptolemy's concept of the world. Thirdly, the results of World Explorations by the Portuguese since the emergence of Prince Henry the Navigator, were kept by the secret policy of the Portuguese government from the eyes of general geographers.

Under the reign of King John I of Portugal, Prince Henry the Navigator warmly received many astronomers, cosmographers, geographers and navigators of the time for exploration of the West African coast, and discovered Madeira, the Azores, the Canary Islands and the Cape Verde Islands. When asked about the territorial rights on these newly found islands, the Pope emitted the opinion that these islands should be made the possession of the discoverer. He also declared all the land to be discovered from then on in the area as far as India should be held by discoverers. The Portuguese, encouraged by this Papal declaration, extended their expedition further south. Bartholomew Diaz reached Cabo Tormentoso (later Cape of Good Hope) on the southern tip of the African Continent in 1487 under the reign of King John II. In 1498, Vasco da Gama arrived at Calicut on the western coast of the long coveted Indian Peninsula. In between these two memorable discoveries was Christopher Columbus' discovery of the New Continent in 1492. It is superfluous to make here a detailed comment on these glorious geographical discoveries, about which a variety of important studies have already been published. Before proceeding to cartographic analysis, let us see what Henri Vignaud, one of the top authorites on the study of Columbus, had to say about the motive of Columbus' Great Exploration project.

Columbus (1451–1506) owed his project greatly to a letter and a map he received from Paolo Toscanelli, a Florence astronomer-cosmographer, in 1474, according to Las Casas, the most reliable recorder of Columbus' life, and Ferdinando, Columbus' son. In his letter to Columbus, Toscanelli said in effect that, since the distance eastward between the western extremity of Europe and eastern extremity of Asia was tantamount to 225° out of the whole circumference of the earth, and thus the distance westward between the same two points was equal to only 135°, the western route was much shorter than the eastern route to countries of East Asia, which were abundant in gold, silver, jewels and spices. This opinion was said to have given impetus to Columbus' urge to materialize his project.

However, Vignaud reached a different conclusion after a thorough study of the letter and its background, and stated as follows: The size of the world Toscanelli stated in the letter was based on the view of Marinus de Tyre (late first century), which became known to the world during the Renaissance. During Toscanelli's days, the stretch between Europe and East Asia was believed to be 140° to 180° in accordance with the traditional concept of the world since the Medieval Age. Meanwhile, there were two kinds of maps handed down from the Medieval Age, the one being Portolanos for navigation in the Mediterranean Sea, and the other, Imago Mundi covering the whole world. While the latter was the product of profound, but imaginary, thoughts of astronomers, cosmographers and philosophers of that time, the former was drawn from the actual experiences of Italian and Catalan navigators. Mediteranean mariners of the time did not believe in such a vast stretch between the East and West as stated by Marinus. The great scholar like Toscanelli, who was versed in Greek and Roman classics and knew about Imago Mundi and Portolanos, must have noticed the mistakes of Marinus. Therefore, Vignaud concluded, the story about his letter to Columbus must be a fiction by Bartholomeo, Columbus' brother.

On the other hand, Las Casas and Columbus' son stated that Columbus' World Exploration was a result of his years of study. They named as books Columbus referred to in his investigations the works of Starbon, Onesicrite Pliny, Nearchos, Esdras, Marinus de Tyre, Alfra-

gan, Aristotole, Averroes, Seneca, Pierre d'Ailly, Jules
Capitolin, Solinus, Marco Polo, Mandeville, Albert le
Grand, Avicenne, etc. Columbus himself quoted more
names of scholars in his own writings. But it is hard to
believe that Columbus had read all the works by these
ancient writers. If he had really studied all these works,
he would not have adopted Marinus' erroneous theory.
In any event, the real manual of his expedition project
can be detected through a minuted study on notes he
jotted down in his favorite books. According to Vignaud's
research, Columbus was most influenced by Pierre d'Ailly's *"Tractatus de Imagine Mundi."* He was also influenced by Pio II's *"Historia rerum ubique gestarum, cum
locorum descriptione non finita,"* and by Pliny's *"Natu-
ralis Historia"* as well as by Marco Polo's Travels and
also Ptolemy's Geography. These, Columbus' favorite
Fig. 4.   books, with his notes, are respectfully preserved today at
Fig. 5.   the Biblioteca Capitular y Colombina in Seville. In any
event, Columbus made the mistake of underestimating
the unknown waters to the west of Europe because he
adopted Marinus' concept of the world through d'Ailly's
work.

Columbus made another mistake about the size of the
earth by minimizing the distance of a degree of longitude
(latitude as well). Columbus set the distance of a degree
at $56\frac{2}{3}$ Italian miles, while scholars of his days estimated
the distance at $62\frac{1}{2}$ or $67\frac{2}{3}$ miles. Columbus himself said
that his measurement of the distance of a degree during
his 1482–1483 expedition to Africa proved the length of

a degree given by Arabian astronomer Alfragan to be right. But Vignaud observed that Columbus had only borrowed the figure from d'Ailly's book. In a nutshell, Columbus adopted the Arabian cartography without due consideration and as a result underestimated the stretch of the unknown part of the world. That was why he set sail on a perilous voyage of the unknown ocean abroad the small 233-ton boat, Santa Maria.

III.   Maps of East Asia in the Age of World Discoveries

There are only a few maps existing today that were drawn in the late 15th and early 16th centuries containing newly discovered areas such as those in and around India discovered by the Portuguese, and the New Continent found by the Spaniards. However, we can get a glimpse of the map of East Asia in the age of World Explorations by the "New Maps" (*Tabula Nova*) supplemented to the edition of Ptolemy's Geography published in 1513 at Strasbourg (though it is believed that the maps were actually published several years earlier) under the sponsorship of René II, Duke of Lorraine (1451–1508). He was a patron of learning with particular interest in cosmography and cartography and was searching for the world map that contained all the recent discoveries made by the Portuguese. He could obtain, from Lisbon through the good office of a certain Italian Benvenuti, a similar world map as the one Portuguese King Emmanuel put up on the wall of his living room, together with the records of the four expeditions by Amerigo Vespucci to the New Continent.

On the basis of these new acquisitions, the *"Hydrographia, sive Charta Marina"* (World Map with the title "Marine Chart") was drawn and included in the above-mentioned "New Maps." Beside these, a more detailed large wood-cut world map entitled *"Universalis Cosmographia"* was published by Martin Waldseemüller (classicized as Hylacolymus) under the patronage of the Duke in 1507. This splendid and long-lost map was discovered in 1901 by Professor Joseph Fischer.

The "New Maps" were repeatedly reproduced, not only in various editions of Ptolemy's Geography such as that of 1520, 1522, 1535, 1541 etc., but also in different editions of Gregorius Reisch's *'Margarita Philosophica'* (first edition: 1515).

"Tabula Moderna India" in the "New Maps" of the 1513 edition shows a great improvement in delineation over the previously published maps on East Asia. In short, they are much closer to the actual conformation. For instance, the Malay Peninsula in the "New Maps" shows an outline and features very much like the peninsula as it is now known, although the southern tip of it is extended down to 14°S. lat. The name "Malaqua" is inscribed on the western coast of the peninsula and on the sea west of the peninsula is an oblong island reminis-
Fig. 6. cent of Sumatra, named Taprobana, although it lies

from northeast to southwest. Except that its southern tip is placed about three degrees north of its actual position, Cape Comorin of India is reproduced with very close resemblance to its actual conformation.

It is amazing that such an advance had been made on the presentation of geographical features of India and Malaya. It is amazing because it was in 1510 that the Portuguese occupied Goa followed by the acquisition of Malacca in the next year and 'Hydrographia' was drawn nearly 10 years before these events. It is presumed that drawing a map of a newly discovered area would take quite a long time after the place was explored. And yet in this case, the Portuguese drew the map a decade before they actually occupied the place. Why?

It is said that King Emmanuel of Portugal sent a spy disguised as a merchant, Pero de Covilham, to Calicut and Goa in 1487, ten years before Vasco da Gama started the expedition to India, to obtain information about these places, and that Vasco da Gama took with him over the refusal of the King of Melinde an Indian-born Arabian sailor by the name of Malemo Canaca who was well acquainted with the Indian Ocean. There is little doubt that the Portuguese had had sufficient information and knowledge about Malacca before they captured the place. There is an interesting episode about a Jew on this point. When Vasco da Gama was leavnig Calicut for home at the end of 1498, he employed a Jewish interpreter who escaped from Poland, where an anti-semitic holocaust took place in 1546. After a long wandering in Palestine,

Alexandria and Cairo, he came to India via the Red Sea. This Jew was converted, and Vasco da Gama gave his name to the neophyte, so he was called Gaspar da Gama or known as Gaspar da India. Vasco da Gama took with him Gaspar, who had a command of several languages and was well versed in Oriental affairs. This Jew played an important role in the Portuguese pursuit of expedition to the East and participated in the expeditions of Vespucci and Cabral. In a letter Vespucci wrote in 1501 which contained information about East Asia he learned from Gaspar, Vespucci mentioned that Gaspar had traveled to Malacca, Sumatra and Java and was well versed in the situations of these places.

These stories substantiate the conjecture that the Portuguese possessed information about Malacca, which was thriving as the emporium for China and the Archipelago, before they proceeded to capture the place. And the Portuguese must have been in possession of quite accurate information about Further India and the East Indies through traveling merchants after they reached India. When these are taken into consideration, one could accept without much wondering the fact that the Portuguese were able to draw a fairly accurate map of the Malay Peninsula and place Malcca at its exact position in *"Tabula Moderna Indiae."*

There are a few other maps, extant, drawn approximately in the same age and presenting an excellent delineation of the Malay Peninsula, for instance, the world maps drawn by Alberto Cantino, Nicolay de

Canerio and Visconte Maggiolo. Cantino's world map was drawn between 1501 and 1502 by a Lisbon cartographer on order from Hercules d'Este, Duke of Ferrara and Modena relayed to him by Cantino, the Duke's envoy to the court to Portugal (now owned by Biblioteca Estense in Modena). From studies on Canerio's world map it is found that it was made sometime between 1502 and 1504, but little is known about Canerio himself (the map is owned by the Archives du Service Hydrographique de la Marine, Paris, of the Navy Department of France).

The Malay Peninsula on these Portuguese maps of the early 16th century is given an outline similar to that found on modern maps. But its southern tip stretches southward far beyond the equator and thus the peninsula as a whole is really gigantic. This imaginary peninsula resulted from the attempt of the Portuguese, who had arrived at Goa, to reconcile the Malay Peninsula they had heard about and the traditional Gigantic Peninsula. Unlike the Indian Peninsula and the Malay Peninsula, this imaginary Gigantic Peninsula was doomed to disappear with the advance of geographical knowledge. For the carotgraphers of Europe who were yet to see Asia east of Malay, putting the real Malay Peninsula and the fantastic Gigantic Peninsula harmoniously together was no easy task. A typical delineation of East Asia conceived by the cartographers of the day was as follows: The Asian Continent has three peninsulas protruding from its southern end, just as if

3 big icicles were hanging from the eaves. The western-most of them is the Indian Peninsula, at the center is a hybrid between the Malay Peninsula and the Gigantic Peninsula and at the east end is a triangular peninsula which also originated from the idea of the Gigantic Peninsula. The east coast of the triangular peninsula runs almost straight from southwest to northeast. Maps with such a delineation of East Asia were made from the 1520's until the mid-16th century.

In order to study old maps of East Asia drawn in the days when important discoveries made in a short period of time were rapidly changing the appearances of the world maps, one must know what relations the carto-graphical changes taking place about the New Continent had on maps of East Asia. At that time, the geography of the West Indies, the coast of the Mexican Gulf, the northern and eastern coastlines of South America and the eastern coast of North America came gradually to be known as a result of a series of explorations led by such explorers as Columbus (1492-1504), Cabot (1492-1498), Cortereal (1500), Vespucci (1502), Pinzon (1500), Cabral (1501), De la Cosa (1501) and Solis (1508). Because this was the time when the size of the unknown part of the world was underestimated, cartographers unavoidably shrunk the unexplored part lying from the west coast of America to the shore of East Asia or put places about which little were known into this unknown section. In such conjectural map drawing, cartographers put an oblong-shaped Japan of Behaim type on a position which

overlaps West Indies. It is a well-known fact that Columbus himself never doubted that Spagnola or Española
(Haiti Island) was Cypango (Japan) throughout his life.
Therefore, for a period of time, cartographers obliterated
Japan from the surface of their world maps because they
could find no proper place to put this island country.
Thus Japan is missing from several dozen maps drawn
at this era, the most representative of which is Johannes
Ruysch's world map (1508), in which things about Japan
were included in Spagnola. A legend inscribed on the
sea—a space of about 20° wide—between a nameless island
(Isabella, now Cuba) to the Northwest of Spagnola and
the eastern point of Mangi (China), where Zaiton
(Chang-chow) is placed, on Ruysch's map, offers an in-
sight into the imagination of cartographers of the day.

It reads: "According to Marco Polo, there is a big
island called Cypango about 1,500 miles east of the port
of Zaiton. He says that this is an independent country
inhabited by idolaters with a king and is not subordinate
to any country. It is very rich in gold and produces all
kinds of jewels. Because descriptions about Cypango including idolatory fit Spagnola, and the position of the
island falls on the island discovered by the Spanish, it is
concluded that the island called Spagnola by the Spanish
is Cypango. Therefore, we refrain from putting Cypango
in addition to Spagnola."

In the early 16th century, geographical features of the
east coast of both North and South America came gradually to be known clearly. After Balboa discovered the

Mar del Zur or Sur (later Pacific Ocean) in Panama in
1513, cartographers were required to put the ocean west
of the New Continent; but because little was known
about the west coast, they had to draw it by conjecture
and gave a very smooth coast line as a result. In addition,
because they still underestimated the size of the unexplored part of the world, the cartographers drew North
America very narrow from east to west, as seen in such
maps as the one by Visconte Majollo made in 1527 (preserved at the Biblioteca Ambrosiana in Milan) and by
Hieronymus de Verrazano drawn in 1529 (owned by the
Biblioteca Vaticana). Scholars studying ancient maps call
this type of America the Verrazano-type.

Maps drawn in this period show the eastern coastline
of the Asian Continent running from southwest to northeast with its northeastern extremity touching the north-
western coast of North America, only separated by a
narrow arm of water. Typical of such maps is Timiripa's,
globe gore (made before 1533). Since this water channel
is nothing but a product of imagination, other cartographers connected the two continents by an isthmus in
the northern Pacific Ocean as seen in the maps of
Johannes Schöner (1523–1524) and Franciscus Monachus
Fig. 7. (1526), etc.

Maps on which the North American and Asian continents are connected can be classified into two categories.
The one includes those done in an earlier period on
which North America and East Asia are so confounded
that many East Asian place-names, including Japan, are

found on North America. The other group includes those drawn at the time when the conformation of Mexico and the western coast of Central America was made clear by the explorations of Cortes (1521–1525) and Guevara (1526), the western coast of South America by Pizarro (1526–1527, 1531–1535) and by Almagro (1535), and the western coast of California by Ulloa (1539) and Alarcon (1540). Because the cartographers of the maps of this later period no longer confounded Asia with North America, they had to find a place where they could place conformations of East Asia once lost from the map. For example, when we talk of Japan, Giacomo de Gastaldi put a small island of irregular triangular shape with the name "Giapam" in the "Golfo de Tonza (Torza)."

This imaginative creator of the fanciful Japan has another creation to his credit. He curved his "Golfo de Tonza" further inward toward the north until it turned into a strait which split the Asian and North American continents and named it "Stretto di Anian." Gastaldi's mistake of calling this strait "stretto di Anian" derived from his erroneous belief that Annam, which is actually to the south of China, is to the north of China. Since this imaginary strait bore a close resemblance to the actual Beering Straits between the two continents discovered by Beering in 1740, it has caused many controversies among scholars. According to recent studies, this idea of Gastaldi was first conceived in 1562. Zalteri's map of 1566 is the first to bear the Anian Straits.

IV.   Influences that the Portuguese Capture of Malacca and Expedition to Moluccas Gave on the Map

After acquiring Goa in 1510 and making it a base, the Portuguese captured Malacca, the distribution center for Southeast Asian trade, in 1511 and immediately sent an expedition fleet of three vessels to Moluccas, a production center for spices, in preparation for a planned capture. A map of Malacca and the East Indies known under the name of Rodriguez, a pilot of one of the vessels, is retained in a reproduction in Viscount Santarem's atlas, published in 1849 in Paris.

Fig. 8.   This is the first map that shows the East Indies. The delineation and placing of the Sunda Islands and Borneo and the locationing of the Molucca Islands are finely done on this map. As a matter of fact, there are many shortcomings and errors. The delineation of the Molucca Islands is inaccurate, Celebes is depicted as a long chain of mountainous islands situated too close to the Molucca Islands resulting in a vacant space on the spot Celebes should be placed, and the name "Maquater" which represents Celebes is given to Borneo. Nevertheless, considering the age when this map was drawn and the fact that this is not the original but a copy, this is amazingly well done, far better than any European-made maps of the day. Santarem estimated that the map was made between

1524 and 1530. Other scholars disagreed and believed
that it was made at the time of the Portuguese expedition
to the Molucca Islands copied from Javanese or Chinese
map.

This theory is based on the following passage in a
letter Albuquerque, the Governor of India, wrote to
King Manuel of Portugal on April 1, 1512:

"Your Majesty, I have the further pleasure of present-
ing a fragment from a large map made by a Javanese
navigator. This map includes the Cape of Good Hope,
Portugal, Brazil, the Red Sea, the Persian Gulf and the
Molucca Islands and shows sea routes to China and Gore
[Loochoo], points where ships pass and the interior of
China and Gore. I have never seen such an excellent
map. I have no doubt that this will please Your Majesty.
Names on the map were transcribed from the original
written in Javanese letters with the help of the Javanese.
This was copied from the original Javanese map by
Francisco Rodriguez. I am sure that Your Majesty could
examine in detail the places where Chinese and Gore
people live, the sea route of Portuguese vessels to the
Molucca Islands, the location of gold mines, the Banda
Islands where nutmeg is produced, Siam and the cape
on the curved part [Ning-po] of the Chinese coast [this
cape is the northern limit for Portuguese ships]. The
original map was lost when the Flor de la Mar was
wrecked. This copy was made by the painstaking efforts
of two pilots, Francisco Rodriguez and Pedro d'Alpoym.
This is a very precious and detailed map showing even

the sea routes to places where the Javanese go. However, islands located in the straits between Java and Sumatra are missing."

This letter is an important document proving how the so-called Rodriguez' map was made. The map of East Indies, reproduced by Santarem, is a unique source extant of the early stage. The inscription on his map is in fine handwriting but hard to read, and few people could read it before Rauffaer. Many modern writers who discussed this map either misunderstood or ignored historical facts to build up dogmatic theories of their own and failed to form a uniform view on it. Their negligence of the history and old maps of East Asia is one cause for this confusion. In addition, the Santarem's reproduced map as well as the map quoted in Albuquerque's letter were called by the same name, "Rodriguez' map" to cause further confusion. In fact, Santarem's reproduction, entitled, "Portolano, drawn between the years 1524 and 1530 by Fr. Rodriguez," is confused with the map mentioned in Albuquerque's letter. However, a comparison between Albuquerque's letter and the writings by Bliller, a keeper at Bibliothèque d'Assemblée Nationale in Paris, where the original maps Santarem referred to were preserved, will show a clear-cut distinction between the two.

What is referred to in this letter as Rodriguez' map which Albuquerque was going to present to the King of Portugal was a *world map,* compiled by Rodriguez and d'Alpoym, from a copy of a map of the East Indies ob-

tained in Java and other materials from other parts of
the world. This world map was compiled during the
period of Portuguese expeditions in 1511 and 1513. The
Javanese map, reproduced by Santarem, is a manuscript
in the form of an atlas consisting of several maps; it was
made sometime after 1520 because a legend on one of
these reads, for example, "A ship started in 1508, passed
the Straits of Malacca and returned in 1520." Therefore,
since the map referred to in Albuquerque's letter has
been lost, the Javanese map retained in Santarem's atlas
is more valuable than the lost world map, so far as the
delineation of the East Indies is concerned. The map
preserved in Paris, which Santarem referred to was not
the real original, of course. It is unnecessary to say that
the original marine chart depicting China, Loochoo and
East Indies, the source of the map preserved in Paris,
was drawn a long time before Rodriguez and d'Alpoym
made their maps in 1511. It could not be considered as
a product of the personal investigations of the Portuguese as a result of their capture of the Molucca Islands.
On the contrary it was made in preparation for their
expedition to the Molucca Islands.

Some of the maps in the manuscript atlas Santarem
referred to have place names in Chinese characters. In
addition, Loochooans' maritime routes are described in
detail in some of these maps as if to indicate who drew
these maps. The recent discovery of the Loochoo's "Collection of Diplomatic Documents" in manuscript revealed Loochooans' intermediate trading activities in

East India and Further India since the 14th century. In addition, Portuguese documents and maps show that there was close contact between the Portuguese and the Loochooans. Thus, there is no doubt about the influence of Loochooan or Chinese marine charts in the map of the East Indies, made known by Santarem.

This valuable Javanese chart known by Rodriguez' name never became known to other countries at that time because the Portuguese jealously guarded their maps from others and kept the sea route to the Molucca Islands in the utmost secrecy.

The influence of the Portuguese capture of Malacca and advancement to the Molucca Islands on the map-making of East Asia would best be known by studying the maps made by the Portuguese authorities of the day. Unfortunately, no map made in those days exists today. The best that could be done is to infer them through the existing official map of Spain, the one made by the Reinels.

Pedro Reinel (Reynel), Sr., a Portuguese cartographer serving at the Portuguese court, was also a well-known navigator. His son, Pedro Reinel, Jr. lived in Seville and served to Charles V. Pedro Reinel, Jr. was engaged in the making of the marine chart to be used for Magellan's expedition. In 1519, his father came to Seville to finish the Molucca Islands part of the marine chart which was in the making by the hand of the junior Pedro. It was about this time that both Spain and Portugal were com-

Fig. 9. peting hard with each other to get competent explorers, navigators and cartographers. It is said that the senior Pedro was summoned by the Spanish King to Seville to finish the map having been drawn by his son, probably because the junior Pedro died before completing the map.

It is very regrettable that the biography of Reinel, who is said to be the founder of the Seville school cartography, has not been clarified. A majority of Reinel school maps were lost in secrecy in Spain with the lapse of time. Although only a few of them remain in Germany, Italy and France, most of them were actually anonymous and are only attributed to the works of Reinels as a result of researches. It is ironical that none of these maps exists in Spain, which was so eager to keep them in secret. Let us study the map of East Asia (c. 1520) now preserved at Armeebibliothek, which is assumed to be the work of Pedro Reinel, Sr.

In Reinels' map, the Malay Peninsula was drawn very broad, with part of a large land showing on the east end of the map across the sea from the peninsula. This land can be recognized as the trace of the Gigantic Peninsula in older maps. While the delineation of Sumatra is fairly accurate, the shape of the Sunda Islands in the east of Sumatra is excessively long in the north to south direction, possibly because the islands were drawn by supposition. Borneo, which was clearly drawn in Rodriguez' map, is missing from Reinels' map, partly because the Portuguese maps of the East Indies were not easily available in Spain at that time owing to the rivalry between the two countries. The absence of Borneo in Reinels' map is being used by some scholars to prove that there is no relationship between Reinels' map and Rodriguez' map.

On the other hand, there are several common or similar points in these two maps. They are Sunda Archipelago, the arch-shaped chain of islands east of the archipelago, a smaller arch-shaped chain of islands, and the Spice Islands in between. Generally speaking, the East Indies part of Reinels' map was somewhat inferior to that of Rodriguez' map. Therefore, chances are that the Reinels took their cue from Rodriguez' map as far as the East Indies part is concerned. It is presumable from comparison between the maps of Reinels and Rodriguez that Pedro, while serving the Portuguese king in Lisbon, might have obtained the part of the Spice Islands from the one line Rodriguez' atlas.

The mansucript Javanese atlas known by the name of Rodirguez is said to be in the possession of Jerónimo Osório (1506–1580), a noted theologian, philosopher and historian. There is little doubt about such data as this Javanese atlas having been held at the Portuguese court, in view of the fact that Osório was contemporary with Emmanuel the Great (reigned 1495–1521) and that 'The Life of King Emmanuel' is one of his most popular works.

Another of Reinels' planisphere (c. 1519, attributed to Jorge), preserved in the Armeebibliothek at Munich set the stretch from the east end of Brazil westward to the

Malay Peninsula at 218°, or 7° shorter than in Canerio's map of Portuguese origin. In Canerio's map, the Pacific Ocean is totally missing, while Reinel's map contains the Pacific Ocean, its western end at 33°N. corresponding to the eastern end of East Asia, and the Spice Islands and neighboring islands are placed near the equator, although the western coast of the American Continent was still unknown. Since the Pacific Ocean was not fully explored, detailed delineation of islands in it was not available at that time. And yet, the map successfully described the stretch of the ocean, though roughly—18° wider than the actual stretch. And this is where Reinels' map was advanced in comparison to the Portuguese-school map. Such was the cosmographical situation preceding Magellan's departure for his circumnavigation of the globe.

V. Magellan's Circumnavigation and Spain-Portugal Scramble over Spice Islands

Ferdinand Magellan (1480–1521), a Portuguese serving the Portuguese King, once witnessed Portugal's expedition to Moluccas, the provenance of spices which were most profitable in trade with East Asia, when he was dispatched to India. Later, he quitted Portugal after having quarrelled with the Portuguese King, and served the King of Spain (the Emperor Charles V). He concluded a contract with the king for his long-cherished enterprise of making an expedition to the Spice Islands from the West in 1518. He owed the successful achievement of his project to the tremendous financial and moral help from his friend, Cristóbal de Haro, a rich merchant with a number of shops in Portuguese India. Meanwhile, Magellan obtained a detailed report on the 1511 Portuguese expedition to the Spice Islands from Francesco Serrão, one of the commanders of the Portuguese expedition, who was Magellan's friend and relative. Therefore, it was natural that Magellan's expedition tour of the Spice Islands, dispatched by the Spanish king, aggravated the rivalry between Spain and Portugal. In addition, Pedro Reinels, father and son, Portuguese cartographers who quit their posts in the Portuguese court and served the Spanish king, drew the map for Magellan's expedition tour of the Spice Islands, as mentioned before. Argensola, the author of the 'Conquista de las Malucas' (1609), said Magellan used Reinels' chart to explain his expedition tour to Charles V.

Magellan's expedition fleet, consisting of five vessels headed by the flag ship Trinidad, left San Lucar on September 20, 1519, crossed the Atlantic Ocean to reach South America, cruised down south along the eastern coast of the South American Continent, passed the straits to the southern tip of the continent (later named after him, then advanced into the Pacific Ocean on November 28, 1520. The fleet advanced northwest, and after finding several small islands, discovered the Archipelago of St. Lazarus (the Philippine Islands) in March, 1521. Magellan was murdered by natives in Matan, a small island near Cebu, but other members of the expedition continued to cruise north of Mindanao to the west. They went down west as far as to Cagayan Island, Sulu Islands, Palawan and Borneo, then managed to reach Tidor on November 8, 1521 where they loaded a quantity of spices, via the southwest of Mindanao. The expedition crew, now aboard the only remaining vessel, the Victoria, under the direction of newly-appointed commander d'Elcano, took the course to west in the Indian Ocean, and found Amsterdam Island (March 1522), turned round the Cape of Good Hope, Cape Verde Islands, then finally returned to San Lucar on November 6, the same year, to complete the first circumnavigation of the world. Greatly satisfied with the sucess of the expedition, Emperor Charles V became enthusiastic about expeditions to the East, and the scramble between Spain and Portugal grew more and more serious for the time being.

Meanwhile, Portugal sent a number of fleets of the Spice Islands after its first expedition there in 1511 in an attempt to establish its power on the islands. Among them was Antonio de Brito, who heard the news from crewmen of a Javanese boat that they had seen a non-Portuguese European vessel enter the Spice Islands. This was when his fleet stopped at a port on the northern shore of Java on its way from Malacca to Moluccas in October, 1521. Surprised by the news, which meant that Magellan's expedition fleet had entered Tidor, the Portuguese launched an attack on Tidor on one hand, and on the other negotiated in 1524 at Badajoz with Spain to decide the demarcation between Spanish and Portuguese territory in these islands. However, the negotiation ended in failure, because Portugal tried to determine the titles of the Spice Islands and the Philippines by the Tordesillas Treaty (concluded in 1494) while Spain claimed these islands to be Spanish territory.

Now, we must touch on the Spain-Portugal demarcation issue of the time. After Columbus' first expedition to the new continent, Spain pleaded to Pope Alexander VI to approve the territorial right of the discoverer to newly-discovered land. The partition line between the land discovered by Spain and Portugal was set at 100 leagues west of Cape Verde Islands by the Papal Bull of 1493, it is said. The story on the demarcation line, thus set by the Pope, is widely adopted by the history text books of the world. In addition, Gerhard Mercator, the famous cartographer, said in a legend in his large-sized world map of 1569 (*"Nova et Aucta Orbis Terrae Descriptio,"* renowned for his projection) as follows: "In the year 1493, when the feverish rivalry in distant navigation was at its height between the Castilians and the Portuguese, Pope Alexander [VI] fixed a meridian circle 100 leagues from any of the Cape Verde Islands, or from any of the Azores, to mark off for each faction its rights in navigation and conquest, allotting the western hemisphere to the Castillians, the eastern to the Portuguese. This boundary, however, was set aside by both factions on account of the disputes that arose, and in 1524 [sic] there was established as their common boundary the meridian distant 370 leagues to the west of San Antonio, the westernmost of the Gorgades."

However, the fact was first revealed by the research made by H. Vander Linden in 1916. According to his study, the Papal Bull of 1493 on the matter had contained nothing mediatory between the two countries and was extremely ambiguous about the concrete boundary. The Papal Bull only stipulated the Spanish sphere as "running from pole to pole 100 leagues to the west and south of any island of the Azores and Cape Verde Islands." The meaningless phrase, "100 leagues to the south" was an expression of Spain's attempt to check Portugal's strong claim on yet unknown land which might be discovered in the south of Africa. In any event, the Pope gave one-sided approval to Spain's claim, instead of taking actual mediatory steps between the two countries.

The partition line was actually established by the Tordesillas Capitulation signed at the conference between the two countries on June 7, 1494. At the conference, Spain conceded a little to Portugal and set the longitude 370 leagues west of Cape Verde Islands. Both countries seemed to have understood that territorial rights in the East Indies should be determined by the date of discovery and occupation by force. As the scramble over the territorial rights to the Moluccas broke out, however, the implicit understanding between the two countries that the above-mentioned boundary set in the

Atlantic Ocean could be applicable on the antipodes in the Pacific touched off a tremendous controversy at the Badajoz Conference of 1524 on the territorial issues over the Spice Islands and the Philippines.

Let us study how the demarcation problem appeared on the official maps of the two Iberian powers made during the thirty years between the Tordesillas capitulation (1494) and the conference of Badajoz (1524).

In a lecture meeting held in 1921 to commemorate Magellan's circumnavigation quatercentenary, Edward Heawood discussed the cartographical significance of Magellan's voyage and the influences the voyage had on cartography thereafter. In the lecture he said: "The position of the demarcation line described as 370 leagues west of the Cape Verde Islands in Cantino's map is too close to the islands no matter from what part of the Cape Verde Islands is it measured. The same is found on maps of the Reinel school. If we transfer this border line to the Canerio's map, it falls, according to the manner of longitude numeration followed by Waldseemüller, in 334° east (or 26° west) of the Canary Islands, and its prolongation on the opposite side of the earth by making this spot as the datum point, would fall in 154° east of the Canaries; that is, on Canerio's map, about 30° east of the center line of the Malay Peninsula. The reason for shrinking the old world from Europe to East Asia and enlarging the unknown Pacific in order to push South American coast-line eastward was probably a political one to move the newly discovered areas in the

South America eastward as much as possible so that might come within the Portuguese hemisphere."

This theory to explain the demarcation line from the political viewpoint is meaningless. Because, no matter how far eastward the Portuguese could have been able to move the east coast of South America, it would bring to them nothing more than a self-contentment on the parchment that had nothing to do with the actual domain. Since the border line is set as 370 leagues west of the Cape Verde Islands, it could be moved to the right place any time when astronomical observation of longitude was correctly done. Also since the circumference of the earth is 360°, the gain one could make by stretching the Western hemisphere is offset by corresponding loss on the Eastern hemisphere.

Let us study the length of 370 leagues once more. The distance between the Cape Verde Islands and the boundary line calculated on the basis of the ration between scales marked on Cantino's map (1501–1502) and the equator and the tropics, becomes 20.1°~20.8°. Computing 1° as 17.5 leagues, the distance becomes somewhere between 352 and 364 leagues. When shrinking of the parchment is taken into consideration, this figure can be said to coincide exactly with 370 leagues. In the case of Canerio's map (1502) on which the border line is not drawn, the distance between the Cape Verde Islands and a spot near Maranhão Bay in South America (the boundary line is estimated to pass over this point) where a Portuguese flag is drawn, becomes 300 to 320 leagues when calculated on the basis of a similar method using scales on the chart. On Reinel's map of 1519 in which latitude and longitude are marked instead of scales, the distance is 21° or 368 leagues; this leaves little doubt that the distance was intended to be 370 leagues. These maps bear no explanations as to the unit of scales. Heawood reached his conclusion that the distance between Cape Verde Islands and the boundary was too small because he calculated counting 1° to be 15 leagues (1 league=4 Italian miles). Actually, the distance was drawn to be 370 leagues as prescribed by the Tordesillas treaty.

This is even more clearly illustrated in three maps by Diego Ribero which incorporated the findings of Magellan's circumnavigation. On these maps, the demarcation line runs near Maranhão Bay in South America, on the east side of which is drawn the Portuguese flag and on the west side the Spanish flag. In addition, two of these maps made in 1529 (owned by the Landesbibliotek, Weimar, and by Vatican, Rome, respectively) state in their title that the map is divided into two parts according to the treaty concluded in the City of Tordesillas. The title in the original runs as follows: *"Carta Universal En que Se contiene tode lo que del mundo Se ha descubierto fasta agora; hizola Diego Ribero Cosmographo de Su Magestad: Año de 1529 ẽ Seujilla:~/La qual Se devide en dos partes conforme Á la capitulaciõ que Hizieron los catholicos Reys de espanã, y El Rey don Juan de portugual ẽ la Villa de Tordessilas: Año de 1494:~//"*.

Ribero's maps have graduations at every 10° on both east and west of the demarcation line on the equator. Following these, let us return to the Molucca Islands on which the two countries' dispute entered. On the Ribero map, the line just on the opposite side of the earth from the demarcation falls on the Molucca Islands. The Spanish apparently did not consider this line as the boundary line as exemplified by the placing of the Spanish flag about 1.5° west of this line. This appears to indicate the Spanish thought that the real boundary could only be drawn by the date of discovery and the use of force.

Diego Ribero was a Portugal-born cosmographer-cartographer who moved to Spain, worked for Charles V and participated in the Reinels' drawing of the chart which was used by Magellan for his expedition. In 1526, Ribero took part as one of the important members (*Piloto de Su Magestad*) in a joint conference called to draw the standard official marine chart (*"Padron Real"*) comprising all newly discovered places. This *"Padron Real"* or *"Padron General"* does not exist today but the above-mentioned Ribero map is believed to be the closest to it.

This map made by Ribero, the first-class cartographer of the day who had all necessary information on the New World and who must have been able to obtain materials from Portugal if necessary (parts about India and Southeast Asia on his map show a good deal of novel Portuguese knowledge) shows most of the Moluca Islands as belonging to Spain. Since Ribero was a cartographer, he was unlikely to move the demarcation line as he liked. Now let us study the demarcation line in East Asia from the present point of view. With the present method of measuring using Greenwich as prime meridian, the demarcation line 370 leagues west of Cape Verde Islands falls on the meridian 46°W.Gr. Therefore, the partition line on the Eastern hemisphere falls on the meridian 134°E.Gr. which passes the western part of New Guinea. This means all such places as the Moluccas, the Philippines, Celebes, Borneo, the Sunda Islands and the Malay Peninsula would come within the Portuguese dominion. However, when Ribero attended the Badajoz conference as an important member of the Spanish commission to decide to which of Spain and Portugal the Molucca Islands and the Philippines should belong, he asserted that the title to these islands should be given to Spain. Was his argument based merely on political motives?

The writer would like to examine the correctness of the longitude of several outstanding points on the Ribero map. Longitudinal errors on Europe and Africa are small and those on America are just a little larger but still small. When it comes to Asia, the errors suddenly become great, in many cases longitudes placed more than 10° off eastward. And the relative positioning of various places in East Asia are firmly acurate, errors seldom surpassing a few degrees. Thus it is obvious that the cause of the errors was in the inaccurate delineation of the Red Sea and Arabia. Furthermore, such places as the East Indies, India and western Asia where Magellan's expedition failed to reach were drawn on the basis of materials obtained from the Portuguese. Therefore, it is certain that the Spanish did not purposely move Arabia out eastward.

What is worthy of special attention is that Timor, the island from which D'Elcano started for Spain, is out of position by about seven degrees towards the east. This smaller margin of error compared with other islands in the vicinity may be an indication that D'Elcano brought back results of his surveys on the point. Anyway, the fact is that the moving of Timor westward by 10° took up the space where the Sunda Islands should be placed and made it impossible to have the islands on the map between Java and Timor.

The utmost accuracy in longitude on maps attained by Ribero, the best cartographer of the day, with the full possession of all available materials, is what we have just reviewed. Spain did not claim her territorial right on Molucca Islands and the Philippines just from political motives. The very cause of the dispute lies in that neither country knew the correct longitude. It can be said that political motives were to be observed more on the Portuguese side because the Portuguese claimed that regardless of the position of the demarcation line in East Asia, the Molucca Islands were theirs. This claim is tantamount to refusal to admit the application of the Tordesillas Capitulation to the Eastern hemisphere.

Let us take a glimpse of maps of the Seville school which followed Ribero. The map of Alonzo de Chaves

(1536–1537) is said to be a copy of "Padron Real," but
does not exist today. According to Wieder, the America
on the map is very similar to that on the map of Lopo
Homen (1554) and the same could be said about the East
Indies. Dahlgren says that Chaves' map could be surmised
from the map of Alonso de Santa Cruz (1542, owned by
the Royal Library, Stockholm). According to Abendanon,
Celebes and Borneo might have been missing from
Chaves' chart as they are from the Santa Cruz map while
both islands are drawn on the map of Lopo Homem.
The Santa Cruz chart does not show much improvement
over Ribero's map. The only improvement observed is
a little more realistic outline given on the southern coast
of Java and the eastern coast of Gilolo (Halmahera). The
better outline of Gilolo was a product of the second
Oriental expedition of the Spanish (1527). Sebastian
Cabot's map (1544) is a large-size copperplate print.
Cabot was an explorer and cartographer who first served
the British King and discovered Labrador and Florida
(1497–1498) while searching for a sea route by way of the
Arctic Ocean to East Asia. He later worked in Spain and
became famous for his expeditions along the basin of La
Plata of South America (1526). East Asia in Cabot's chart
also follows Ribero's pattern. The world map (1540–
Fig. 10. 1545) of Pedro de Medina, preserved in the National
Library, Madrid, is a valuable material for showing the
extent of early knowledge about the west Pacific Ocean
at the final period of Spanish-Portuguese dispute.
Medina was an excellent mathematician, geographer and

cartographer at the same time, and his *"Arte de Navegar"* was translated into many languages to become the textbook for navigators.

VI. East Asia on the Maps of the Dieppe School of North France

As reviewed in the previous pages, maps of the East Indies in the 1520's when Portugal-Spain disputes raged culminated in the maps of Diego Ribero, the great leader of the Seville school. However, for about thirty years from the Ribero school maps to Portuguese maps that appeared in the mid 16th century to which we will refer shortly, no new knowledge and information about the East Indies or Southeast Asia are found in the maps of either country. Fortunately, this lack of new information is compensated for by a group of maps drawn by artographers of the Dieppe or Norman school of North France. According to the studies made by Father Anthiaume, about thirty of these maps were drawn in the 16th century and about twenty were made in the 17th century. Among others, the maps by Desceliers, Desliens and Rotz in the 1540's furnish important information.

Maps of the Dieppe school clearly are of Portuguese origin. Some scholars believe that these were based on the knowledge and information brought back by experienced Norman seamen who traveled aboard Portuguese vessels. Characteristics of East Asia on the maps of the

Dieppe school include the influence of the so-called map
of Rodriguez and his follower Reinel on the conformation of the part from the Sunda Islands to the Molucca
Islands, the influence of the maps of Rodriguez and his
follower Ribero as for Gilolo (Halmahera), the reappear-
ance of Borneo which was missing from the map of
Reinel and was incomplete on maps of Ribero and other
cartographers of the Seville school, and the inclusion of
Fig. 11. Celebes which was missing from Spanish and Portuguese
maps until then. As for the Philippines, only Mindanao
and neighboring islands are represented and Luzon Island is missing as in the Spanish and Portuguese map.
The conformation of the Malay Peninsula up to Indo-
china is similar to that of Ribero's map and names of the
places on the Asian coast are marked up to the vicinity
of Canton.

Another distinct feature of the Dieppe school maps is
that Java faces to one of three peninsulas that radially
protrude from a continent extending in a sphere from
the Antarctic up to about 40°S. lat. and that the other
two faces to the southern tip of Africa and South America, respectively. This imaginary "Austral Continent" is a
product of the thinking of Greek and Roman philosophers based on the so-called "Law of Analogy" of
Aristotle. That is, they thought that since there is a big
mass of land like Eurasia and Africa on the northern
hemisphere, there must be a continent of similar weight
for the sake of balance. This product of imagination was
given new life when the Magellan Straits were discovered

and "Tierra del Fuego" was witnessed southwest of it, as Fuego was interpreted as a part of the "Austral Continent." Depicting of the imaginary "Austral Continent" is a common phenomenon found on many world maps drawn in the 16th and 17th centuries. Even names are found on this phantom continent on Dieppe school's maps. Toward the end of the 16th century an ocean was observed in the west, and also in the south, of Tierra del Fuego. Then in 1615 Cape Horn was discovered by Le Maire and Schouten and it was established that Tierra del Fuego was an island. But even after that, this strange continent remained on maps. The imaginary continent which persistently existed on maps finally disappeared by the mid 17th century following the discoveries of the Torres Straits, Tasmania, New Zealand and the coastline of Australia.

VII. Influence of Portugal's Trade with China and Japan on the Maps of East Asia

After the occupation of Malacca, the Portuguese made their inroad to the South China Sea (1513, 1514). A Portuguese trade investigation mission, dispatched by Albuquerque, Viceroy of India, reached Tamão, near Canton in 1516, and the fleet of the Portuguese King's mission arrived in Canton and obtained a license for trade and commerce from the Chinese government in

1517. However, the spoliation and territorial infringement by the Portuguese in Tamão angered the Chinese in 1518. Tamão was besieged and attacked by the Chinese in 1520, and the Portuguese there fled to Malacca. In 1522, a group of the Portuguese landed in Tamão and invaded Macao, but was driven out soon.

The above-mentioned Spanish maps of the Ribero type contain the cartographic knowledge thus obtained by the Portuguese who arrived at the Chinese coast during these ten years. China on these maps is dotted with several Chinese place names. However, in the area north of Canton in these maps, there are only a few unidentifiable place names and one or two place names stated in Marco Polo's Travels. Latitudes in these maps are fairly accurate, though.

From 1540 on, the Portuguese appeared again in Liampo of Che-kiang Province, near Ningpo, by the help of Chinese merchants in the East Indies. They used the Chinese in the coast area as their agents for trade with inland China, and promoted their trade activities by bribing Chinese government officials. As trade with China at Liampo developed well, the Portuguese entered Chincheo (Chang-chow) in Fu-kien Province by the same strategy from 1544 on. Smugglers were rampant between Japan and China and the China Sea was infested with pirates at that time. And the Portuguese took advantage of the anarchic situation in the China Sea coast area to develop their trade with China. However, they were again ousted from Liampo in 1548 and from Chincheo in 1549.

There are no Portuguese maps of East Asia drawn in the 1540's, existing now. As was mentioned before, however, the delineation of the China coast at that time was left to posterity by the maps of the Dieppe school. The maps of the Dieppe contain more place names on the China coast than those of the Ribero school, in which Chincheo is on the northern extremity. Their conformation was also more accurate than that of the Ribero maps.

Meanwhile, the Portuguese also appeared in waters near Japan at that time. It was in 1543 that the Portuguese drifted to Tanegashima Island, south of Kyushu, and introduced muskets to Japan, according to Japanese documents. It is known that Portuguese vessels visited Kyushu ports continually after that. Since Japan had not closed its door to the world yet, Western civilization was brought to Japan by the Portuguese. Consequently, the cartographical rendering of the Loochoo Islands, Japan and Korea offered naturally an important subject for Portuguese cartographers.

The Portuguese maps of East Asia at that time can be divided into the following four types by the delineation of Japanese islands, which was very characteristic of these maps:

(i)   Mercator-type maps; a group of maps represented by the conformation of Japan in the map drawn by *Fig. 12.* Gerhard Mercator (1512–1594), a well-known Dutch cartographer. In these maps, Japan is shaped like a horizontal oval. In the north of Japan is a train of small islands called *"Ilhas de Miacoo,"* while in the southwest is a chain of small islands, bearing the place names "Lequio Major" and "Lequio Minor." As a matter of fact, Japan's delineation of this kind was already shown in the world map in two hemispheres by Ruscelli, inserted in the Venetian version of Ptolemy's Geography (1561, 1562, etc.). Both Ruscelli and Mercator might have followed some Portuguese model like the grand maritime chart (1545–1548), now preserved in the Vallicelliana Library, Rome. This chart is a Portuguese anonymous and undated manuscript map.

Mercator, who was versed in classic geography, attempted to identify the ambiguous place names of classic writers with the place names on the newly drafted Portuguese maps of East Asia. Consequently, his map of East Asia turned out to be a strange mixture. Thus, his rich knowledge of classic geography all the more confused posterity. After Mercator's map was printed, it was later reprinted or recopied into sixty different kinds.

The names, "Lequio Major" and "Lequio Minor" in this type of maps seem to have been adopted from a Chinese source; the Great and Small Liu-k'ius are the names given to the Loochoo Islands and Formosa during the Ming dynasty. The oval form of Japan in this type of maps appears to have been copied from Chinese maps, because it is the usual habit with the Chinese to depict islands in oval form. It is conceivable that the map might have been drawn before the Portuguese set foot on the Japanese shores. Fernão Perez de Andrade who heard

about the wealth in Loochoo dispatched Jorge Mas-
carenhas from Chincheo (Chang-chow) to Loochoo (1517)
in an attempt to conquer the islands. However, Mas-
carenhas failed to reach Loochoo because of the adverse
wind. In addition, the Japanese word, "Miyako" is seen
in this type of maps. Therefore, this type of maps is not
necessarily the product of imagination alone, but is believed to be drawn on the basis of hearsay of Japanese
mariners or Chinese merchants in Southeast Asia. Maps
in this group did not represent Korea yet.

(ii)   Homem-type maps; a group of maps represented
by the maps drawn by Lopo Homem (1554) and by Diogo
Homem (1558). All of the 20 odd existing maps of this
type are hand-written and not printed. In these maps,
Japan is drawn as a peninsula, protruding from the east
end of the Asian Continent southward into the sea. This
shape appears to have been patterned after the Japanese
map of the Gyogi type, a traditional schematic map which
was popular among the Japanese at that time. However,
researchers have so far failed to detect the influence of
the Gyogi map on this type, because of the fact that the
principal axis of Japan was erroneously set from south
to north and that Homem, in drawing his map, made
use of the geographical situation (latitude) and rough
outline of Kyushu upon information from the Portuguese, and gave an exaggerated indentation to the coast
lines in an attempt to make it harmonious with other
parts of the map. The geographical situation of the
Loochoo Islands in the maps was so accurate that it can

be easily identified in comparison with modern maps.

(iii)   Ortelius-type maps; a group of maps represented by the delineation of Japan in *'Theatrum Orbis Ter-rarum'* (1570), the atlas by Abraham Ortelius (1527–1598), a noted Dutch cartographer comparable with Mercator. This atlas was published in 40 large-sized editions and more than 30 small-sized editions and was also translated into many languages of the world.

Ortelius copied the delineation of Japan from Ho-mem's map and changed the principal axis of Japan from the south-north direction in Homem's map to the east-west direction. However, Ortelius' map of Japan is significant in that it was printed and adopted widely in a variety of geography books later and became very popular.

(iv)   Dourado-type maps; represented by the maps drawn by Lazaro Luiz (1563), Fernão Vaz Dourado (1568) and several others. Of about 40 kinds of existing maps of this type, only a few were printed and all others were handwritten. The conformation of Japan in this type is very characteristic in that the Tohoku (Northeastern) District on the east end of horizontally-drawn, thick Honshu Island is turning down to south in hook-shape (actually, this part should be turned to the opposite di-rection), with Kyushu in rectangular form protruding southward from the western end of Honshu. Shikoku, on the other hand, lies rectangular-saped beneath Honshu, about halfway between the Tohoku District and Kyushu. Why, then, was the geographical situation of Kyushu and

the Tohoku District erroneously drawn in this type of
map? The Tohoku District in the Gyogi maps was usually
drawn comparatively small in size and with little swerve
to the north. In some of the Gyogi maps, copied by the
Chinese, such as the "Map of Japan," in 'Jih-pên-kuo
ch'iao-lüeh' (Concise Treatise on Japan) by Hsüeh Chün,
the Tohoku District is drawn bending to the south. This
treatise was published as a Chinese strategical manual
against attack by Japan, immediately after the riot caused
by the Japanese in Ningpo in 1523 as an open protest to
the unreasonable treatment given to Sosetsu, an official
mission from a Japanese war lord in Yamaguchi Prefec-
ture, western Honshu, to Ming court. This treatise has a
preface dated 1523 and 1530. The original Chinese version was lost, but two copies of its Korean edition (1565)
are now preserved in Japan. It is not clear whether or
not the Portuguese at that time drew their maps of East
Asia on the basis of this map. However, it cannot be
denied that this map bears a close resemblance to Dourado-type maps as far as the delineation of Japan is
concerned. The geographical situation of islands of the
Loochoo chain in Dourado-type maps is as accurate as
in Homem-type maps.

Of these four types of Portuguese marine charts, the
Homem and Dourado-type maps are more significant
than the other two types, in terms of their value as
cartographic data, since the first two kinds of maps
presented Portuguese personal observations in East Asia
more effectively. Moreover, the maps of the other two

types, of Mercator and of Ortelius, are nothing but com-
pilations based upon second-hand sources. Of the first
two kinds of maps, the Homem-type maps were forgotten
only about 30 years, while the Dourado-type maps
lived about one century. In this regard, the Dourado-type
maps are typical of the Portuguese charts of the 16th
century. These were also used by Dutch and British
navigators to the East. For instance, William Adams who
came to Japan in 1600, Don Rodrigo de Vivero y Velasco
(1609) and John Saris (1613), as well as Sebastian Viz-
caino who explored gold and silver islands near Japan
in 1611, all used this type of charts. This type of chart
was also used for the time being by the trading fleets of
the Netherlands, the only European country which
maintained trade ties with Japan after Japan took an
isolationist policy.

VIII.   Spain's Jealous Attachment
to Spice Island

Gonzalo Gomez de Espinosa and some other members
of Magellan's expedition who stayed on the Spice Islands
explored the Western Pacific during a period between
April and October, 1522. But they were captured by
Brito upon their return to Gilolo, and taken to Ternate,
then sent back to Spain. The Portuguese base in the
Moluccas was in Ternate Island, while Spain was trying
to set its base in Tidor Island, a small island south of

Ternate. Therefore, the two powers were exposed to the constant danger of a frontal clash with each other. As was mentioned before, Spain and Portugal failed to reach any concrete accord on the title of the Spice Islands at the Badajoz Conference of 1524. King of Spain, Emperor Charles V, sent the second Spanish expedition fleet to the Spice Islands in 1525 to bolster its foothold in the Archipelago. The fleet of seven vessels under the command of Francisco Garcia Jofre de Loaisa left Spain in July and arrived in Tidor on December 31 of the same year, but all vessels but the flag ship, Santa Maria de la Victoria, were lost in the long voyage of trials and hardships. Commander Loaisa died on May 26, 1526, during the voyage. D'Elcano who took the place of Loaisa also died on August 4. The ship arrived in Ladrones on September 4, and in Mindanao in early October. However, they retreated in the face of strong resistance from natives and because of the food shortage, and headed for Cebu, but were blown by the reverse wind to Molucca. This was on December 31, the same year that the ship finally anchored in Tidor. During this voyage, Martin de Uriate, a navigation officer, drew a map of the Gilolo coast and noted in his logbook his discovery of Papua (New Guinea), which had thus far been unknown. After their arrival in Tidor, the Spaniards were under constant threat of attack by the Portuguese and the natives, with only slight hope of the arrival of rescue parties from Spain.

Charles V dispatched the third Spanish expedition

fleet from Spain's new colony, Nueva España (Mexico), to the Spice Islands in order to help the members of the second expedition team left on Tidor Island. Alvaro de Saavedra, heading a fleet of three vessels, left the port on October 31, 1527. Two of the three vessels of the fleet were lost in a storm on December 15, but the flag ship continued its voyage and arrived in Ladrones on December 29. The flag ship of the rescue fleet, searching for the Spaniards left marooned on islands, arrived in Tidor to meet the compatriots in June, 1528. As they were easily discouraged by the overwhelming power of the Portuguese there, the Spaniards tried to retire from the island and set sail to return to Mexico. But the ship was driven out of its course by headwind and drifted to the east coast of New Guinea, from where the ship sailed northeastward to discover the Caroline Islands (named in 1686 in honor of Charles II), then was blown back again to Tidor. In May, 1529, Saavedra headed for Mexico by himself, leaving Hernando de la Torre and several soldiers at Tidor, and discovered the Marshall Islands. However, he died during the home-bound voyage, and other members of his expedition had to return to Tidor. As the Portuguese based at Ternate took advantage of this opportunity to attack Tidor, the Spaniards finally discarded Tidor and took refuge in Samfor in the east of Gilolo, then settled down there temporarily with the expedition that Spain would begin peace negotiations with Portugal.

Menezes, Governor in Ternate successfully drove all

the Spaniards from Tidor. But Portugal proposed in the Saragossa Conference in 1529, in fear of possible revenge by the Spaniards in the future, that she would pay indemnity to Spain on condition that Spain withdrew its territorial calim to the Spice Islands. Portugal knew Spain's financial difficulties at that time. The negotiations were successful. Charles V agreed to waive Spain's territorial right to the Spice Islands for an indefinite period for an indemnity of 350,000 ducats paid by Portugal. In the conference, the partition line between Spanish and Portuguese territory in the area was set at 17° east of Moluccas. The Portuguese promise to give full convenience to the repatriation of the Spaniards in Moluccas was not observed immediately. It was in 1534 that they were permitted to return home. They were first sent to Cochin in India in 1536, then repatriated to Europe in several groups. De la Torre had Urdaneta, who was repatriated earlier than Torre, carrying a detailed report on the circumstance of the Spanish exploration and maps home to present to the King. However, these materials were confiscated by Portuguese police in Lisbon, and Urdaneta narrowly returned home in February, 1537, with much difficulty.

Undaunted by consecutive failures in two previous attempts to bolster its power in the Spice Islands, Spain sent a fourth exploration fleet, headed by Ruy Lopez de Villalobos, from Navidad (Mexico) in November 1, 1542 with the objective of planning a colony in the *"Islas del Poniente"* ("Western Islands" i.e. the Philippines). Vil-

lalobos arrived in Mindanao the following year and
stayed a year in Sarrangani, a small island south of
Mindanao, to tap possibilities for colonization of the
Philippines. The results of his investigation turned out
to be unsatisfactory, and the Portuguese Governor in
Ternate ordered Villalobos to leave there and return
home. Villalobos first refused to take this order, but as
he had a short supply of food for his fleet and was asked
for help by the chief of Tidor, he at last entered the
Portuguese territory, and arrived in Tidor in 1544. He
then met there crewmen of the S. Juan, which was dispatched from Sarangani to Mexico the previous year.
The ship had earlier returned to Tidor as it failed to
reach Mexico. In the following year the Spaniards were
entirely exhausted. Commander Fernão de Sousa de
Tavora of Ternate at that time issued a strict order,
"Return to Spain Immediately, Villalobos!" The Spaniards surrendered. Villalobos passed away on the way
home, and the remaining members of his expedition
barely arrived in Spain in 1547 and 1548.

Thus, Spain sent four expedition teams to the Spice
Islands during the twenty years between Magellan's
voyage and Villalobos' expedition, and had fierce battles
with the Portuguese each time. In addition, there were
several expedition plans that had not materialized during this period. Although all of Spain's persistent efforts
to recover the Spice Islands ended in failure, the Spanish
expeditions there brought about a variety of important
geographical discoveries and cartographical contributions

and left memorable traces in the history of the Pacific Ocean.

IX. Spanish Rule over the Philippines

The failure of Villalobos' expedition put a tentative end to the Spain-Portugal struggle over the Spice Islands. At that time Charles V, King of Spain and concurrently Holy Roman Emperor, possessed vast territory in the New World and boasted being the world's strongest national power. Consequently, he was in constant clash with King Francis I of France and invoked four wars with France. In the meantime, the religious reformation movement took place. Thus, Charles V spent most part of his life in ceaseless territorial struggles with Portugal, until he was hit by a sickness in 1556 and turned over the Throne to Philip II. Spain remained silent for more ten years. However, the new king resumed an active colonial policy.

In 1559, Philip II ordered Governor-General of Mexico to dispatch an expedition fleet to plant a colony in the Philippines. Urdaneta (1498–1568) who had already joined the second and the third expedition was credited with having been an excellent Naval officer with broad knowledge of navigation and geography. When the fourth expedition was being mapped out, he was in Mexico. Therefore, the King requested him to take command of the expedition to the Philippines.

However, since he had already determined or a religious life and actually had been in the priesthood of the Augustinian Order since 1553, he at once declined the request. As a result, the King appointed Miguel Lopez de Legazpi (1501–1572), another well-known Naval officer with a good strategic career, as commander, and had Urdaneta assist him.

They left Navidad in November, 1564, leading the fleet of four vessels. The fleet arrived in Cebu Island of the Philippines in April, the following year. Realizing that Cebu Island was an ideal site as the base for Spanish colonial policy in the Philippines, they conquered the island and built a fort there, then named the place *"Santissimo Nombre de Jessus."* This was the first Spanish colony in the Philippines. After exploring near-by islands for several years, the Spaniards occupied Manila in June 1570, and moved their base from Cebu to Manila the following year, then built a new center of the colony. Then, Martin de Goiti's squadron conquered central Luzon, while Juan de Salcedo occupied northern Luzon in 1572 and 1573, conciliating the natives and winning the confidence of the islanders successfully.

When Portugal protested that the entry of the Span-iards into the Philippines constituted a violation of the Saragossa Agreement, Spain rebutted that the Agreement was concluded as to the territorial dispute over the Spice Islands and not over the Philippines. After all, the ulti-mate way to settle the difference of views was by force. Spain owed the success of its colonization of the Philip-

pines in the face of Portugal's resistance to the skillful
colonial administration by Lgeazpi as well as to the
discovery by Urdaneta of the Pacific route connecting
the Philippines and Mexico, which enabled constant
supply of man power and goods to the Philippines. The
Portuguese were dominant in the Spice Islands because
they had secured the supply lines from their bases in
Africa and India. But finally, Spain established a colonial
foothold comparable with Portugals in the Pacific, thanks
to the successful connection of the Philippines with
Mexico.

After setting up a base in Cebu Island, Legazpi sent
Urdaneta to Mexico to report the result of the expedition in the Philippines. Until then, the Spaniards had
never succeeded in their attempts to reach Mexico from
the Spice Islands on their return voyages. But Urdaneta
made it for the first time. Leaving Cebu Island on June
1, 1565, Urdaneta cruised up northward via Ladrones *Fig. 13.*
(Mariana Islands) to meet the northwesterly wind, and
spotted a certain cape of Japan (possibly Cape Inubo) at
36°N., but he did not meet the northwesterly wind
until he reached 40°N. or thereabout (he went further
north to 43°N. at times), where he took the course to the
east. It was on October 3 that he arrived safely in Aca-
pulco Port. In other words, he made use of the Japanese
Current, North Pacific Drift and California Current on
his return voyage. These currents in the Pcafiic and the
northwesterly wind are being used by modern steam
ships on Pacific voyages today. But the discovery of these

navigation factors was really a tremendous advantage
during the day of sailing vessels.

Urdaneta logged in detailed the important data he
obtained through observations and experiences during
the return voyage in his vayage journal and drew a
marine chart of the route. Spain kept in top secret
Urdaneta's marine chart, which played a vital role in
Spain's colonial policy in the Philippines, and took every
possible step to prevent details of this chart, from leaking out of the country. Even a single copy of this marine
chart of that time does not exist now, possibly because
of this extreme secret policy of Spain. However, the
years of the secret policy collapsed when the chart, confiscated from the Galleon ship on the Philippines-Mexico
route by Capt. George Anson in June, 1743, was published in Anson's *Voyage round the World*.

On account of the Spanish secret policy, there exist no
Spanish marine charts of the Pacific Ocean drawn in the
16th and 17th centuries now. The only maps of the kind
now available are those drawn in the 18th century. Besides Anson's map, there exist the following ones: the
manuscript copy which La Pérouse obtained from a
Spanish ship in Monterey (near San Francisco, California) in 1786 and published in his *Voyages*; the manuscript copy, reproduced in color by Dahlgren in 1900,
which is now preserved in the Library of Academy of
Sciences, Sweden, and is believed to be drawn sometime
between 1716 and 1720; the marine chart of the western
Pacific by Miguel Elorriaga in 1709, and the marine

chart of the whole Pacific Ocean with the Philippines-Mexico route drawn on it, by Francisco Xavier Estorgo y Gallegos (1770), which are preserved in the Archivo General de Indias at Seville.

In these Spanish maps, numerous islands are drawn alongside the Philippines-Mexico route. However, most of these islands were not found by 18th and 19th century explorers and navigators, who had searched for these islands on their voyages. This was partly because of the difficulties in determining longitude at that time and of naive traverse sailing. It also happened that the same island was drawn in different places in respective maps by different persons. Magellan determined the longitude of Ladrones at 176° west of Canary Island, or 22 degrees shorter than in the modern maps. This proves how difficult it was to determine longitude at that time.

X. Iberian Cartographers' Contributions to the Mapping of East Indies

While the Portuguese reached the Spice Islands through the Indian Sea, availing themselves of the monsoon on their voyage, the Spaniards got to the Spice Islands via Magellan Straits and on the equatorial current, evading the Portuguese sphere of influence. And both of them drew charts of their respective routes and their vicinity. They made every possible effort to obtain materials needed for drawing these maps, even by stealing maps of the other's, and to protect their own maps from leaking to the other. Nevertheless, the practical value of these maps declined bit by bit as the political situation and the content of these maps changed with the elapse of time. In addition, since the official maps were drawn only in small quantity by a limited number of qualified cartographers, few original maps were handed over to posterity. Only a limited number of them were brought to other European countries and published in Italy and in the Netherlands, where the publication of maps was popular at that time. It is by means of these maps that the history of cartography can be narrowly reconstructed. Therefore, it happened that Portuguese maps were transmitted by the Spaniards and vice versa. Eventually, these maps were transmitted to the hands of their enemy, against whom they had attempted to keep their maps in top secret.

Now, let us review the changes in old maps of East Asia in accordance with the Spanish history of Pacific exploration. The Mariana Islands first appeared in the Ribero maps of 1529, which contained the results of Magellan's exploration voyage. The Mariana Islands in these maps are composed of only two small islands named "Ladrones." Magellan, in fact, arrived at Saypan and Tinian in March 6, 1521, and recognized Aguigan in the near-by waters, then named these islands *"Islas de las Velas Latinas"* or *"Ladrones."* The present name, the Mariana Islands, was given in honor of Maria Anna de Asturias, widow of Philip II, in 1668. In Santa Cruz' map (1542) of the late Ribero school, Ladrones were drawn as a chain of small islands running from north to south. The chain of small islands was drawn with more distinction with names of respective islands, in Sevastian Cabot's map of 1544. Espinosa, one of the survivors of Magellan's exploration team who remained in the Moluccas, discovered four other islands of Ladrones, and returned to Tidor, where he was captured by the Portuguese. He was repatriated to Europe by force and was robbed of his logbook and marine charts. This incident may be responsible for the fact that some of the Portuguese charts of the 16th century contained the early conformation of Mariana. Since seven of the Mariana Islands were first discovered by the first Spanish expedition, then known to Portugal, it may be that Portuguese maps were the first to contain an early conformation of the Mariana Islands and that later materials on the islands were not referred to. As all the Spanish vessels for the East Indies cruised with the Mariana Islands as their target, it is conceivable that each expedition dropped in on the Mariana Islands.

Ladrones in these charts took two different delineations. The one, named *"Restinga* (reef) *de Ladrones,"* is depicted as a group of small islands, as seen in Portuguese planishpere, preserved in the Vallicelliana Library in Rome [1545–1548], and other 16th century Dutch printed maps originated from the Portuguese sources. The other is shaped like a chain of small islands running from north to south. This conformation, seen in maps of the Ribero school earlier, was also inherited in a number of Portuguese charts after the Homem-type maps, and handed down through the centuries, eventually replacing the charts with Restinga. The chain-shaped archipelago in early Portuguese charts (mid 16th century) was drawn from heterogeneous materials of different kinds. For instance, all islands and archipelago located between the Loochoo Islands and the Mariana Islands are titled en masse *"Os Lequius"* (Loochoo) in Lopo Homem's map of 1554, while Andreas Homo called Mariana *"Ynsulae quae Dicuntur Lequios"* (islands called Loochoo) in the legend in his map of 1559. They must have confused these two islands because of the similarity in their conformation. But the source is so apparent now.

Meanwhile, maps drawn after the mid 16th century contain such islands as Malabrigo, Abreojos, Dos Hermanas, Los Volcanes and Farfana in between Mariana and Japan. These islands, discovered by Villalobos' subordinate explorer Berardo de la Torre on their way back to Mexico, are the Japanese Bonin Islands now. Although the voyage to Mexico ended in failure, the discovery of these isalnds is memorable in that it was the first discovery of Japan by the Spaniards, and that it took place the only two days after the famous discovery of Japan by the Portuguese.

"S. Bartholome," discovered in 1526 by the second Spanish exploration team to the Spice Islands, seems to be the Marshall Islands (named after an English navigator, Capt. Marshall in 1788) today, while "De Sequeira," the island discovered by subordinate officers of Menezes, Portuguese Governor of Ternate in 1525 appears to be in the southern part of the Marshall Islands or in the eastern part of the Caroline Islands. If these were the Marshall Islands, the Portuguese found them a year earlier than the Spaniards. Meanwhile, Saavedra, too, discovered the Caroline and the Marshall Islands during the third Spanish exploration voyage. The Caroline Islands, such as Arrecifes, Matalotes, Jardines, Corales, Reyes, Martires, S. Barnabè, etc. found in the Portuguese charts of the mid 16th century, were mostly discovered by Villalobos in 1543. Later, Legazpi (1565), Drake (1579) and Quiros (1595) visited Reyes, which is now believed to be Palao (Pelew) today. It is next to impossible to identify with accuracy these islands located in the waters on the stretch of 25° long. from Palao to Ponape, only from the old descriptions which used ambiguous measurement.

The Philippines appeared first in the maps of the Ribero school. These maps cover such islands as southern Samar, southwards of Bohol and Cebu, the southeastern coast of Palawan, Mindanao and neighboring small islands, which Magellan and his successors had passed by, plus the northern shore of Borneo and the western coast *Fig. 14.* of Gilolo, with detailed depiction of Moluccas. This is the first cartographic rendering of the Philippines with realistic and positive knowledge.

Meanwhile, the Philippines in the Dieppe school maps

consists of hook-shaped Mindanao and four islands of
rectangular and triangular shape in the north of Mindanao. The four islands are, from west to east, Negros,
Cebu, Bohol and Leyte (or Leyte and Samar amalgam-
ated into one island). To the west of these Islands lies
Palawan. In addition, several place names are entered on
these islands. Since these maps were not drawn on the
basis of actual surveys, they are incomplete in terms of
cartographical rendering. However, the outline of these
islands was all closed and their relative position is good
enough. In this regard, these maps are regarded as the
second stage of the realistic maps with positive knowledge.

On the next stage was a group of Italian maps which
originated from the Dieppe school maps or the Portuguese maps, after which the maps of the Dieppe school
are believed to have been derived. About twenty kinds
of these maps are known now and they were widely
circulated, for they were printed since Gastaldi's map
(1546). Delineation in these Italian maps is almost equal
to that in the Dieppe school maps. Then come the fore-
runners of the Portuguese maps of the mid 16th century.
Among them are the map of the Vallicelliana Library
and Homem-type maps. In these the delineation of
Mindanao is improved very much.

It goes without saying that geographical discoveries
between Magellan's and Villalobos' expeditions were
incorporated in these maps. It is strange, however, that
one of these Portuguese maps contained an entirely novel

delineation of the Philippines, which had not been seen
in Spanish maps. The new conformation of the Philippines was featured by a long and thin island, spanning
from southwest to northeast between 9° and 21°N.,
which lacks the outline of its northeastern shore. The
southern end of this strange island corresponds apparently to Palawan in the maps of the preceding age,
but the northern part shows the prototype of Luzon,
according to its legend. From the legend on this island
in Dourado-type maps it may be inferred that, "Poro
(Pedro) Fidalgo was driven to Luzon by a storm when he
attempted to cruise to Lamao aboard a Chinese junk."
It was in 1544 that the Portuguese returned to Macao
and were officially permitted by the Chinese government
to engage in trading activities there. Chêng Shun-kung's
'Jih-pên-i-chien' ('Japan at a glance,' a directory of Japan,
1564) said a group of the Chinese, together with some
Japanese, sailed to Lamao in the same year. Fidalgo
seems to have drifted to Luzon about the same time as
the Portuguese settled their colony in Macao. The oldest
map of about twenty kinds of this type now existing is
that of Lazaro Luiz (1563). Therefore, the supposition
that this map was drawn a few years after Fidalgo's
incidence is in accord with historical fact.

In the last stage of the Philippine maps, the conforma-
tion of Luzon, the main island, has been completed.
While Legazpi was conquering the northern half of
Luzon Island, after setting the capital in Manila, in 1571,
Limahon, the notorious pirate leading a group of many

Chinese and Japanese, established a fort in Luzon and resisted the Spaniards hard. This pirate was reported to be rampaging in Manila Bay in 1574. Chances are that the conformation of Luzon Island was completed only after the Spaniards quelled the pirates, sometime in late 1570's or early 1580's.

The complete delineation of Luzon Island was first seen in the maps by Bartolomeu Lasso of 1590, J. Martines of 1591 and Petrus Plancius of 1592. Plancius drew his world map on the basis of Lasso's world map, the first map to contain a complete delineation of Luzon Island, but both of these maps were long-lost. Fortunately, however, Plancius' printed world map as well as Lasso's manuscript map similar to the lost original map were discovered by Wieder recently, to give new light on the study of Spanish maps of Luzon, which had thus far been lost to the world. On the contrary, the recent studies have revealed to us the important fact that the existing marine charts used by the mariners of *Goshuin* (literally 'August Vermilion Seal' i.e. Shogunal trading certificate) ships (licensed Japanese trading ships) during a period between the conquest of Luzon by the Spaniards and the time of Lasso's map, give the delineation of the Philippines at that time.

New Guinea was discovered by Menezes, who arrived in western New Guinea in 1527. Later, Saavedra discovered the eastern half of New Guinea, then one of the Villalobos' troups led by Yñigo Ortiz de Retez (Rota) made a fairly detailed survey on its northern shores. The oldest map (1545–1548) of New Guinea, preserved in the Vallicelliana Library, is believed to have been drawn on the basis of Yñigo's expedition. New Guinea was still believed to be part of the vast unknown "Austral Continent" at that time, Spain tried to make use of this land as a foothold for colonial policy in the Philippines, and sent Alvaro de Mendaña on an expedition to New Guinea from Peru twice. In the first expedition, Mendaña discovered the Solomon Islands (1567). Twenty-eight years later, he set sail on his second expedition to New Guinea with the objective of planning a colony there. But he failed to locate New Guinea this time, and instead discovered Santa Cruz Island and Marquesas Island at 50° to 60° east of New Guinea in 1595. As he was killed by the natives on Santa Cruz Island, his wife Doña Isabel Barreto took command of the expedition fleet and continued the expedition through untold dangers and hardships. The Solomon Islands were first covered in the Italian maps of Antonio Millo (1582–1583), but fifteen years after the discovery of the islands. This time lag may be attributable to the general indifference to the political significance of the islands and also to the time needed for the Spanish data to be transmitted to Italy.

XI. Maps Used by the Japanese Licensed Trading Ships

The two Mongolian invasions of Japan (1274, 1281) forced the Kamakura Shogunate to make a great expenditure for defence and finally caused its downfall, civil wars and impoverishment of the people ensuing. In an attempt to secure a better living, the exhausted people in the western part of Japan started surreptitious trade with the Chinese Continent. When they met resistance, these traders restored to violent means to achieve their objectives so that they came to be called "*Wako*" or Japanese pirates. On the other hand, the Loochooans were engaged in trade at the beginning of the early 14th century, playing the role of intermediary in trade among Southeast Asia, China and Japan. Their business activities became more active after the Ming dynasty took command of China in 1368. The area the Loochooans covered in their trade activities extended to such southern countries as Luzon, Annam, Siam, Malacca, Sumatra and Java, and their acting in the area commenced earlier than that of the Japanese proper. It was not until the 16th century (end of the Muromachi Shogunate) that the Japanese advanced to these regions for trade, pressed by the need to open up a new market. The Chinese, who became aware of the fact that the Japanese pirates were making use of the monsoon and sea currents to ransack the Chinese coast, took every precaution against attack by the Japanese trader-buccaneers and had such generals as Yu Tai-yu and Ch'i Chi-kueng make the so-called "Big sweep" (1563–1564). Now that trade with China became no longer possible, the Japanese traders opened business with Chinese merchants in Formosa, Luzon, Annam and other Southeast Asian ports. As soon as Toyotomi Hideyoshi (1536–1598) controled all of Kyushu in 1587, he expelled all Christian missionaries from Japan by order but kept his hands away from trade and left it as it was. In the following year, he issued an order to prohibit piracy and announced that violators of the order would be severely punished. He supported and promoted foreign trade, however, and when he moved to Nagoya in Kyushu to command his armies sent to Korea in 1592, he called eight influencial businessmen of the nation to his camp and granted them a license to engage in foreign trade. The selected businessmen were: Chaya Shirojiro, Fushimiya and Suminokura of Kyoto, Iseya of Sakai, and Suetsugu Heizo, Funamoto Yaheiji, Araki Sotaro and Itoya Zuiemon of Nagasaki. By this step, Hideyoshi introduced the Government licensing system into Japan's foreign trade which until then had been conducted on a purely private basis. When Tokugawa Ieyasu established the Shogunate, he saw the importance of foreign trade and followed Hideyoshi's policy in encouraging the traders. As a result, Japan sent more than a dozen ships each year for trade to such places as South China, Annam, Tonking, Cochin-China, Cam- *Fig. 15.* bodia, Siam, Malaca, Formosa, the Philippines, Borneo and Moluccas in 1603 until the Tokugawa Shogunate closed the doors to foreigners by order in 1636. These trading ships are the ones known as *Goshuin-sen* or the Japanese licensed merchant ships. The activities of these licensed trading ships between 1604 and 1616 can be known today through the original diplomatic documents kept at the Nanzenji Temple in Kyoto which took charge of the original licenses at that time. Official records after 1616 are missing but scholars have pieced together fragmental documents of licensed ships being preserved in various collections and have been able to establish a rough outline of licensed trade activities of the period after 1616. The Japanese merchants who went abroad on these licensed vessels set up Japanese communities in foreign port cities and actively engaged in economic, political, military, cultural and religious affairs even after all the help from home was cut because of the closed-door policy.

The Tokugawa Shogunate destroyed all the data concerning the licensed merchant ships under the isolationist policy. It was only through the painstaking efforts of a number of scholars that much of the trade records before the closing of the doors was reconstructed. Most helpful materials were old documents preserved in Europe including records of Christian missionaries to Japan. Getting the full picture of the Japanese licensed trading ships thus is very difficult. But the excellent researches by Prof. Motojiro Kawashima and Prof. Seiichi Iwao have recently brought many new facts on this subject into light.

On the other hand, materials on maps used by the licensed trading ships are almost non-existent. All these known today are charts of Asia and East Asia—four originals and ten copies. By original is meant here merely those charts which were actually used by the seamen of the day. In addition to these, there are two originals and three copies of Japan marine charts—named "Portuguese Style Japan Charts"—which are in close relation to the charts just mentioned. These two originals were made of parchment following the pattern of European maps for practical use. In total, there are no more than 20 documents on the maps and all of these existing maps are anonymous and undated. Therefore, it is open to question whether these charts were really the maps used by the Japanese licensed trading ships, and unless this is estabilshed, the contents of the charts could not be discussed.

It is believed that these Japanese charts are anonymous because those who drew them were lower-class sailors employed by the shipowners, and the people of the day did not consider such charts to be art objects, especially since they were copies of the Portuguese original with some modifications and additions. Such objects were hardly considered as products of intelligent work meriting the drawers' signature on them, it is believed. Except for these charts, maps were drawn in Japan generally by artist painters. Those drawn by the first-class painters and made into folding screens for interior decoration were valued highly. Thus map drawers of the Japanese charts could hardly be compared with those of Portugal and Spain known as *"Cosmographo de Su Magestad"* who were first-rate scientists with high social positions.

The historical background of these existing charts is known only to a limited extent. Itoya's chart shows that the businessman got the license from Hideyoshi in 1592 and used his chart ever after that. Sueyoshi (or Hirano) Magozaemon (1570–1617) obtained a license for trade with Luzon, Siam and Annam in 1604 but he never visited these places himself. His chart is still being kept by his decendants in Osaka. Materials show that Sueyoshi's map was used between 1604 and 1617. Kadoya Shichirobei (1610–1672) lived in Cacciam (Quinam) of Annam ruling as the head of the Japanese community there. He married a native princess and spent his life there even after Japan cut all ties with foreign countries; he sent his map back to Matsuzaka, his home, via a merchant ship. The maps were used between 1631 and 1636. These are the only maps the historical background of which is known today.

Conformations on these maps show that the maps were drawn after the Portuguese charts of the mid 16th century inserting the depiction of Japan, Korea and Formosa from native sources by the hands of the Japanese. Only the chart of Itoya bears a signature: "SEBASTIAO, AFEZ," but the signator is unknown. Comparison with European maps shows that delineations of the Sunda Islands and New Guinea on these Japanese charts correspond to those drawn between 1545 (Vallicelliana map) and 1590 (Lasso map), delineations of Borneo and Celebes correspond to those drawn between 1582–1586 (Millo maps), and delineations of Luzon correspond to those drawn between 1585–1587 (the map in the reports of Bishop Salazar when Japan-Philippines relations were first established). The delineation of Japan is that of the map in the late 16th century known as the type of maps of the period of Civil Wars (15th–16th centuries) and Korea is based on charts of the early 16th century. Formosa is drawn in an eggplant like shape showing much improvement over the Formosa on the Dourado type map. Place names are written in Japanese phonetic symbols transcribed from the Portuguese sound but for major regions are left in the Portuguese spelling. The Portuguese letters are not found on later maps.

These maps of Asia and East Asia are in close relation to the so-called "Portuguese style Japan charts." But except for one which materials show to have been copied in 1638, none of the other maps could be traced to its date of copying. In any case, these are special charts of Japan made after the Portuguese method of mapping.

Scales are marked on some of these maps of Asia, East Asia and Japan. To know what these scales represent, we must examine scales on many European maps since the 16th century. Most of these European maps use the distance measuring unit of their own country for one degree of latitude and longitude. For instance, $1° = 17.5$ miles in Spanish and Portuguese maps' scale. The same one $1° = 15$ miles in German and Dutch maps. Now the

Japanese charts' scale is that of the Portuguese-Spanish type in which 1° is 17.5 miles. This means that these Japanese maps came from the Portuguese origin.

Now a vellum chart named "Chart for Oriental Nations" owned by the National Museum in Tokyo has a second scale of 1°=45 in addition to the one, 1°=17.5. No unit with such a figure is known in Europe. A clue to understanding this scale is found in a passage of 'Namban-unki-sho' ('Portuguese Astronomical Treatise') by Christovão Ferreira (1580–1652) which read: "One degree is 45 *ri* of a road in five provinces near the capital." The author was a Christian missionary who came in Japan in the early 1610's. He mastered the Japanese language and became well acquainted with things Japanese. When he met with severe oppression by the Tokugawa government, he abandoned Christianity. He changed his name into the Japanese name Chuan Sawano. He married a Japanese woman and became an official of the Japanese government. Thus his observations of Japan are very credible and his mention of the Japanese unit of one degree indicates that the unknown scale marked on the "Chart for Oriental Nations" was an original, Japanese unit of 45 *ri*.

Another important document shedding light on this problem is a rutter or sailing guide ('*Genna-kokaiki*') obtained by Koun Ikeda from Manuel Gonzalo, a Portuguese navigator. This guide, written in 1618, the same period as the chart in question was drawn, says that one degree is 41 *ri*, 31 *cho*, 6 *tan*, 5 *ken*, 3 *shaku* and 5 *sun* in

Japanese scale. Since one *ken* in the measuring is 6 *shaku* and 5 *sun*, while the same is 6 *shaku* in the measuring of Ferrera, an adjustment is needed. And the adjusted figure shows that one degree as prescribed in Koun's guide becomes $1° = 45.37$ *ri*, just about the same as that written by Ferrera. On some of the maps known as '*Piroto no Ho Karuta*' ('Chart for Pilots') one degree is clearly set as 43.75 *ri*. On the vellum-made "Japan Chart" kept by Baron Mitsui and "Chart of Japan" owned by the National Museum, one degree is set between 32 and 33 *ri*. These two figures appear strange because they do not fit the above-mentioned Japanese unit of *ri* nor any of known Western measuring units.

However, the books on weights and measures by Teki-sai Nakamura (1629–1702), writer of great erudition, and by Genkei Nakane (1662–1733), mathematician and astronomer, explain this mystery. They say that there were three kinds of *ri* used by the Japanese of the day. One used by the residents of eastern Japan was made up of 36 *cho*, another used by the people of western Japan which had 48 *cho* in one *ri*, and the nearly extinct 6 *cho-*1 *ri* unit used by the people of a small part of the Kanto District. Nakane writes that one *ri* of 48 *cho* became almost extinct in the Genroku era (1688–1703). Now the strange one degree of 32 to 33 *ri* is a result of having used this 48 *cho-*1 *ri* scaling. By recalculating this figure by the 36 *cho-*1 *ri* system, one degree comes between 42.7 and 44 *ri*, matching the unit of Ferrera, 'Chart for Pilots' and Koun. Judging from this fact, the maps owned by the Mitsuis and the National Museum in Tokyo were either made or used in western Japan.

Although the life of these maps was rather short—less than half a century between the establishment of the license trading system and the closing of the country—there was a change in the cartography of these maps during this period that cannot be ignored. While the Japanese copied faithfully the Portuguese maps, except for the delineation of Japan, Korea and Formosa, during the reign of Hideyoshi (1592–1598), one can see considerable progress in the delineation of the southern part of Hokkaido during the reign of Ieyasu (1600–1616), and they used both scales of Portuguese miles and Japanese *ri*. After that a great number of charts were drawn during the period up to the closing of the door to foreigners. In all of them only the areas concerning the trade of the *Goshuinsen* are drawn. All these maps are nothing but copies of Portuguese maps. The "Portuguese Style Japan Charts" are drawn following the Portuguese method of map-making by determining the geographical position of a place from astronomical observation. It is to be marvelled that the charts should reveal to us so wonderful a conformation that cannot be distinguished by non-professional eyes from that in the maps drawn by Tadataka Ino (1745–1818) who drew them after 18 years' assiduous, actual surveying of the Japanese coasts. Indeed, when we examine the latitude of several points in the "Portuguese Style Japan Charts," we are impressed with their accuracy. For instance, the southern and northern

tips of Kyushu are on their correct position. The southern tip of Kishu is only a few minutes off the correct
position and at the northern end of the Tohoku District
we can find an error by some ten minutes or half a
degree. The Japanese maps of this kind are considered
to have been drawn since the 1610's, though the existing
copies are products after the 1620's. They all have the
Japanese *ri* as its scale. This change shows that the Japanese made the art and technique of map-making of their
own within only thirty years after they imported them
from the Portuguese.

However, cartographical technique deteriorated sharp-
ly after isolationism became the national policy of Japan.
This is illustrated by a childish, clumsily drawn map of
East Asia which was made in 1680 by the magistrate's
officials of Nagasaki—40 years after Japan closed her
doors—for questioning seamen from the Batan Islands
(between Formosa and Luzon) who drifted to the shore
of Hyuga in Kyushu.

*   *   *

The European technique of cartography was never
transplanted to any people of vast Asia, and maps of
Asia were made exclusively by the Europeans, especially
the Portuguese and the Spanish. The single exception
was the Japanese who learned the technique and applied
it to map drawing of their own country. It was regrettable that this technique had but a very short life, stifled
by the isolationism of the Tokugawa Shogunate, and
failing to make any constructive contribution to the

cartographical history of the world. The European style of cartography—characterized by the use of coast lines with the consideration of the longitude and latitude—had its origin in Portolano born in the Renaissance in the Mediterranean Sea area. Therefore, the history of maps of East Asia outline in this booklet may be said to be a history of "maps seen from the ocean."